Chr[...]

Carrie,

I hope you enjoy this
Book, It looks like your
Kind of Story!

♡ Mommy

TROY

Homer's
Iliad
Retold

TROY

Homer's
Iliad
Retold

DAVID BOYLE AND
VIV CROOT

General Editor
MICHAEL J. ANDERSON
Illustrated by
SARAH YOUNG

BARNES & NOBLE BOOKS
NEW YORK

This edition published by Barnes & Noble, Inc.,
by arrangement with THE IVY PRESS LIMITED

2004 Barnes & Noble Books

M 10 9 8 7 6 5 4 3 2 1

ISBN 0-7607-5672-4

Excerpts from the *Iliad* in this volume have been taken from the
1890 revised edition of *The Iliad of Homer: A Translation* by John
Graham Cordery (first published in 1871).

This book was conceived, designed, and produced by
THE IVY PRESS LIMITED

Creative Director: PETER BRIDGEWATER
Publisher: SOPHIE COLLINS
Editorial Director: JASON HOOK
Design Manager: SIMON GOGGIN
Project Editor: CAROLINE EARLE
Designer: ANDREW MILNE
Illustrator: SARAH YOUNG

Printed in China

CONTENTS

INTRODUCTION

Michael J. Anderson

Achilles the demi-god, son of King Peleus and the immortal Thetis. The greatest of all the Greek warriors, he was the brooding presence behind the action of most of the poem, because he sat sulking in his tent, consumed with anger against Agamemnon, refusing to fight.

HOMER'S *ILIAD* and *Odyssey* have long been counted among the earliest masterpieces of the Western literary tradition. The tragic playwright Aeschylus pays tribute to his epic predecessor by calling his own plays "slices of the banquet of Homer." The philosopher Socrates in Plato's *Republic*, while censuring Homer's unbecoming portrayals of gods and heroes, nevertheless cannot deny the overwhelming charm and beauty of Homer's poetry. So venerated, in fact, was Homer that Greek authors could refer to him simply as "the poet," and his esteem as an originator and a worthy subject of emulation has endured to the present age. Vergil's choice of the *Iliad* and the *Odyssey* as models for his *Aeneid* affirms their canonical status among Roman authors. Dante, despite not having read Homer in the original Greek, places him among the five classical laureates the pilgrim encounters in Limbo. And imitation of Homer stands side by side with Biblical tradition in Milton's *Paradise Lost*. In more recent times, James Joyce has domesticated Homer's Odysseus in *Ulysses*, rewriting the Greek hero's journey to the far reaches of the world and back as a day in the life of a Dublin newspaper employee. And Caribbean poet Derek Walcott's sonorous *Omeros* recasts Achilles and Hector as fishermen on the island of Saint Lucia. Despite the considerable political and cultural shifts that have taken place since its composition in the late eighth century BC, the poetry of Homer remains today a moving expression of human experience. The *Odyssey* has at times enjoyed wider appeal thanks to its wily protagonist, its abundance of love and adventure, and its happy ending. The *Iliad*, with its bleak assessment of human life, offers instead an enduring paradigm of tragic suffering. The authors of the present volume provide a contemporary retelling of this story, in language designed to be accessible and appealing to modern audiences, while the addition of substantial excerpts from J. G. Cordery's 1871 translation evokes the poetic grandeur of the Greek original.

The invocation of the Muse in the opening lines of the *Iliad* announces the poem's principal subject:

> *The Wrath, that rose accursèd, and that laid*
> *Unnumber'd sorrows on Achaia's host,*
> *Sing, heavenly Muse—the Wrath of Peleus' Son!*

This wrath (the Greek word is *menis*, pronounced may-nis) manifests itself not as unrestrained physical violence, but rather as smoldering resentment against a perceived injustice. In the first book of the poem, Agamemnon, leader of the Greek forces fighting at Troy, is compelled to return his recently captured concubine Chryseis to her father, a priest of Apollo, in order to appease the god's anger. Infuriated by this loss and the accompanying disgrace, he threatens to take the concubine Briseis from Achilles, one of the army's greatest champions. In response, Achilles would have drawn his sword and attacked Agamemnon on the spot but for the timely intervention of the goddess Athena, and he resolves instead to withdraw his support from the army and sit idle in his camp, certain that his absence will bring hardships to the Greeks and bitter regret to Agamemnon.

This conflict introduces us to the magnificent, yet exceptionally self-centered, heroes of the Homeric world. A privileged elite, mortal though descended from the gods, these heroes risk their lives in battle in return for high social honor (the Greek word is *time*, pronounced tee-may). The hero's honor is regularly confirmed tangibly through the distribution of the spoils of battle, including armor and other treasures, as well as human captives. The quarrel between Achilles and Agamemnon over the captive Briseis is a case of conflicting claims to honor. Nestor, the wise elderly statesman of the Greek forces, pinpoints the essence of the dispute while trying unsuccessfully

Zeus, the king of the gods and ruler of Olympus. His actions and interventions throughout the war dictated much of the dramatic action described in the Iliad. *Here he is flanked by several of the poem's important protagonists: the Atrides, Agamemnon (left) and Menelaus (right); Helen, wife of Menelaus, daughter of Zeus and nominal cause of the war (right); and Leda (left), queen to Tyndareus of Sparta and mother of Helen, by Zeus.*

to resolve it. Achilles, he observes, is the mightiest warrior among the Greeks, while Agamemnon holds the greatest political and military power. Agamemnon's loss of his prize Chryseis, a tangible marker of honor and high social status, threatens his political authority, while Achilles' loss of Briseis detracts from his reputation as foremost champion. Unfortunately, in so passionately asserting their individual claims to honor, both heroes neglect their responsibilities to the larger community of warriors.

The poem initially offers us a more favorable and more intimate view of Achilles' position in the dispute than of Agamemnon's. When intervening in the conflict, the goddess Athena honors Achilles by appearing to him alone, not to his opponent, and promises him rich compensation for the present insult. After Achilles withdraws to his camp, we glimpse a more vulnerable, childlike, human side to the magnificent warrior, as he cries by the seashore and seeks consolation from his mother, the ocean nymph Thetis. And Thetis secures a promise from Zeus himself, the king of the gods, to restore her son's honor. By contrast, the deceptive dream Zeus sends to Agamemnon and his bungled attempt to stir the discouraged troops to action *(Book 2)* hardly characterize Agamemnon as a capable leader. And Agamemnon's army suffers dearly during Achilles' absence from the battle. One by one the principal warriors are wounded as the Trojans push closer and closer to the Greek camp. Ultimately, however, it is Achilles who suffers most in the aftermath of the quarrel, and in his obsessive determination to preserve his honor, he loses his dearest companion, Patroclus. While Achilles, consumed with hatred for Agamemnon, sits idle, deaf to the entreaties of Agamemnon's ambassadors *(Book 9)*, the compassionate Patroclus is moved to tears by the distress of his former comrades. If Achilles' wrath prevents him from furthering Agamemnon's goals, Patroclus argues, at least he can permit his friend to relieve the Greek army by driving the Trojans back. And so with Achilles' assent Patroclus enters the battle and briefly enjoys spectacular success by killing Sarpedon, only to die shortly afterward at the hands of Hector *(Book 16)*.

The death of his closest friend irreversibly alters Achilles' attitude toward the war and toward his own role as warrior. His overwhelming grief wrenches him from his selfish preoccupation with honor and forces him to react to the death of a fellow human being. Acknowledging his own failure to support and protect Patroclus from harm, he resolves to return to the battle and avenge his friend's death, and his quarrel with Agamemnon, judged trivial in comparison with his present loss, quickly fades into the past. Despite this abrupt change of action, however, Achilles remains the same single-minded, obsessive character whose unrestrained wrath nearly destroyed the Greek army. Still subject to overwhelming passions, he exchanges his former smoldering resentment for a burning desire for vengeance, and as vehement as was his wish to see Agamemnon humiliated is his newly acquired hunger for punishing Hector. Returning to battle, he behaves like a one-man army, inflicting massive slaughter on the Trojans and flooding the Xanthus river with blood and corpses *(Book 21)*. Finally, after all the other Trojans have fled to the safety of the city, he confronts Hector, slays him, and taunts his dying enemy with a reminder of Patroclus' death and a threat to feed his body to dogs and birds *(Book 22)*.

Athena, the goddess of war and wisdom, played a major role in the Iliad. Despite being revered and worshiped in Troy, she actively supported the Greek faction. She was a frequent visitor to the battlefield, where she inspired the rank and file with her great battle cries and offered tactical advice and practical assistance to individual warriors, targeting or deflecting spears and arrows, and sometimes riding alongside them in their war chariots.

> *Fool! For, though he were dead, a mightier far*
> *Was yet aboard the galley left unslain*
> *The avenger of his blood, ev'n I, who now*
> *Have slack'd thy limbs. Thou therefore shalt be toss'd*
> *To vultures and to dogs the carrion prey,*
> *But he be laid with honour in his grave.*

Not sated by Hector's death, he shames Hector's corpse by lashing it to his chariot and trailing it across the plain. And after Patroclus' funeral he drags his enemy's lifeless corpse repeatedly around the tomb of his absent friend, unwilling to concede that no punishment, however severe, can heal the pain of his loss. In short, Achilles is a deeply disturbed hero, driven by noble sentiments to atrocious actions, overwhelmed simultaneously by ardent love and ferocious hatred.

In the final two books of the poem, Achilles slowly overcomes his debilitating grief and anger as he releases for burial the two corpses still resting in his camp, those of his dearest friend and his most hated enemy. His farewell to Patroclus' corpse is precipitated by a poignant visit from the ghost of his fallen companion, who urges Achilles to conduct the funeral quickly and thereby let him pass through the gates of the underworld. Achilles' monumental anger is still clearly evident at the funeral, which is accompanied by the horrific sacrifice of twelve Trojan captives, but a more peaceful atmosphere surrounds the ensuing athletic competitions held to honor Patroclus' memory. Here Achilles furnishes the Greek heroes an opportunity to pursue their quest for individual honor apart from the bloody combat of the war. And while he refrains from competing in the events himself, Achilles' presiding role affirms his own prestigious standing in the army. The release of Hector's corpse in the last book of the poem is an analogous, though more delicate, operation. Again Achilles receives instructions from a visitor, this time his mother Thetis, who informs

Hector, the hero of Troy, brother to Paris, who stole Helen from Menelaus and brought the wrath of the Greeks down on the city. For most of the action in the Iliad, Zeus supported Hector, using him to further the plan to bring honor to Achilles. Hector fought to his death in defense of Troy, sacrificing himself and his family in vain—it was the will of the gods that Troy be destroyed.

her son that the gods are angered by his mistreatment of Hector's corpse. Subsequently, the aging Priam embarks upon a dangerous and painful journey to Achilles' camp to offer countless ransom for the return of his son's corpse. Humbly beseeched by the king of Troy, Achilles once again enjoys honor and recognition of his power and authority, and moved by the recollection of his own aging father, he pities his enemy and accedes to his request. He even consoles Priam with reflections on the tragedy of human life and with a magnanimous invitation to end his fasting and partake of food, thereby underscoring his own release from mourning for Patroclus and his own reintegration into the society of the living. To be sure, it would be difficult to read in this episode the transformation of Achilles into a wholly compassionate hero, as his potentially violent anger still lies just beneath his composed demeanor. Nevertheless, his own suffering has given him greater insight into the hardships of human life and the inevitability of death, as well as an ability to acknowledge and pity the suffering of others.

In the *Poetics*, Aristotle justly praises the *Iliad* for the unity of its plot. Rather than attempting to record the entire Trojan War or the life of Achilles from birth to death, the poet crafts a coherent story around a very small segment of the war, the events immediately preceding and immediately following Achilles' loss of Patroclus. Yet within the limited time-span of the plot, the poet repeatedly invokes the broader mythic tradition surrounding the Trojan War and alludes to events ranging from the judgment of Paris, the distant origin of the conflict, to its eventual conclusion with the capture and destruction of Troy. The many allusions to a longer span of time enrich the present narrative of Achilles' wrath immeasurably, imparting to the poem as a whole a quasi-historical realism and injecting into specific scenes the pathos of the irrecoverable past and the inescapable future. Book 3 is particularly retrospective. Here the duel between Paris and Menelaus, a surprisingly late inspiration after nine years of fighting, reminds us that the war began simply because Paris abducted Menelaus' wife. And as she views the battleground from the walls of Troy, Helen wistfully remembers happier days in Sparta and curses herself for having abandoned her former home and husband. But that past is now lost forever, and the poem quickly returns us from the distant indiscretions of Helen and Paris to the devastating destruction their actions currently inflict on others. Paris' romantic indulgence now jeopardizes his entire family and city, and the dutiful Hector is compelled to pay the ultimate price for his brother's recklessness. As he awaits Achilles before the city gates, Hector briefly ponders the possibility of returning Helen and sharing Troy's wealth with the invaders, but he knows it is too late for peaceful reconciliation (*Book 22*).

Achilles may originally have sailed to Troy to aid in the recovery of Helen, but the war has assumed a more personal significance for him since the death of Patroclus, and neither time nor the wrath of Achilles can be reversed.

The bleak future also looms large in the poem, and although the narrative closes with the burial of Hector, the poem emphatically anticipates disasters yet to strike both sides. Tradition records that Achilles died while fighting at Troy, the victim of an arrow shot by Paris and guided by Apollo, and the *Iliad* constantly reminds us of the hero's imminent death. Achilles has learned from his mother that he will die young while at Troy should he choose to fight there *(Book 9)*, and he willingly accepts this fate when he takes up arms to avenge Patroclus. Desperate to prevent the death that awaits her child, Thetis keeps him from the battle for as long as she can and then she provides him with protective armor crafted by the divine smith Hephaestus *(Book 18)*. Paradoxically, the depiction of the world with which Hephaestus adorns Achilles' shield encompasses the full spectrum of human activity and includes both a city at war and a city at peace, but Achilles, who bears this life-encompassing shield, will experience at most half the life it represents. As Achilles mounts his chariot to engage the Trojans, one of his immortal horses is miraculously endowed with speech and reminds Achilles that he too, like Patroclus before him, is destined to die a violent death *(Book 19)*. And with his dying breath Hector accurately predicts that Paris and Apollo will bring Achilles' life to its end *(Book 22)*. Achilles' death, moreover, is eerily prefigured in the death of Patroclus, who falls through the agency of Apollo while wearing Achilles' armor *(Book 16)*. Despite the divinity of his mother and his own success in defeating his enemies, Achilles himself is emphatically subject to the limitations of his mortality, confronted now by the painful and irrecoverable loss of Patroclus and repeatedly forewarned that his own death will follow shortly. As some consolation for his sacrifice he wins honor for himself and for his friend, as well as everlasting fame in the form of poetry (in Greek, *kleos*). But immortality, at least according to Homer, lies beyond the reach of the heroes.

Most of the Iliad *is taken up with graphic descriptions of men killing and dying; sometimes the pages seem to weep blood. The brutality, the terrible exhilaration, and the heartbreaking pity of war is described in a way that transcends time and culture; the weapons may have changed, but men die today in the same glory and agony.*

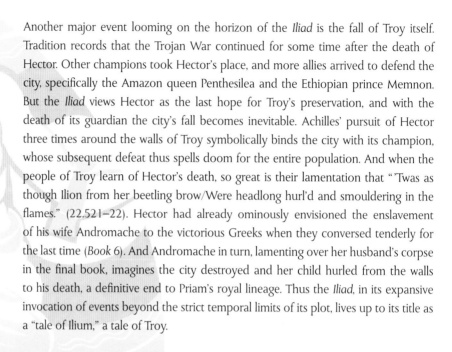

Another major event looming on the horizon of the *Iliad* is the fall of Troy itself. Tradition records that the Trojan War continued for some time after the death of Hector. Other champions took Hector's place, and more allies arrived to defend the city, specifically the Amazon queen Penthesilea and the Ethiopian prince Memnon. But the *Iliad* views Hector as the last hope for Troy's preservation, and with the death of its guardian the city's fall becomes inevitable. Achilles' pursuit of Hector three times around the walls of Troy symbolically binds the city with its champion, whose subsequent defeat thus spells doom for the entire population. And when the people of Troy learn of Hector's death, so great is their lamentation that " 'Twas as though Ilion from her beetling brow/Were headlong hurl'd and smouldering in the flames." (22.521–22). Hector had already ominously envisioned the enslavement of his wife Andromache to the victorious Greeks when they conversed tenderly for the last time (*Book 6*). And Andromache in turn, lamenting over her husband's corpse in the final book, imagines the city destroyed and her child hurled from the walls to his death, a definitive end to Priam's royal lineage. Thus the *Iliad*, in its expansive invocation of events beyond the strict temporal limits of its plot, lives up to its title as a "tale of Ilium," a tale of Troy.

The Olympian gods who oversee and at times participate in this war inspire fear and respect rather than love or admiration. At times they are credited with wisdom superior to that of mortals. A perfectly composed Athena intervenes in the dispute between Achilles and Agamemnon to preserve peace among the Greek chieftains (*Book 1*). And the Zeus who agrees to Thetis' request to restore honor to Achilles also knows in advance the high price Achilles will pay. More commonly, however, Homer portrays the gods as exaggerated forms of the self-centered heroes, immortals with extraordinary strength, power, beauty, and an overwhelming preoccupation with their own honor. Apollo afflicts the entire Greek army with a plague because Agamemnon has dishonored his priest *(Book 1)*. So savage is Hera's hatred of Troy that she would sacrifice her three favorite cities to Zeus, if only he should grant her wish for Troy's destruction *(Book 4)*. She and Athena harbor such intense hatred for Troy not because the Trojans are immoral or impious, but because Paris once slighted them by awarding the apple of discord to Aphrodite instead (24.32–40). The gods display some of their worst manners when wrangling among themselves. Hera constantly chides her husband for protecting the Trojans. On one occasion she stoops even to seduction to draw his attention away from the battle *(Book 14)*. And Zeus, the irascible father of the divine family, repeatedly threatens violence to keep his kin in line. Violent comedy erupts when he permits them to assault each other freely. Athena pummels Aphrodite and knocks her to the ground together with Ares, and Hera boxes Artemis' ears with her own bow (*Book 21*). More disturbing than these family squabbles is their fraudulent and biased intervention in human conflicts on behalf of their favorites. Before Euphorbus and Hector wound and kill Patroclus, Apollo strikes the armor from his body (*Book 16*). Appearing to Hector in the guise of his brother, Athena deceives him into ending his flight and entering an impossible duel with Achilles (*Book 22*). Then she conveniently returns Achilles' spear after he casts at Hector and misses, but no god stands by Hector to return his spear. Nevertheless, as deeply as such interference may offend our notions of fairness, a god's presence should also be viewed as conferring honor upon the favored hero, exalting rather than belittling his endeavor. And divine intervention underscores the significance of climactic events like the deaths of Patroclus and Hector, marking the monumentality and inevitability of the hero's downfall. In short, these gods are a mixed bag. Rarely can we identify closely with such powerful beings, although we may at times laugh at their follies. How seriously we may take them varies with the context and tone of the narrative.

As with the Old English *Beowulf* and the Old French *Song of Roland*, the authorship of the *Iliad* is not accurately known. The blind bard Homer is a figure of legend rather than of flesh and blood, and the fact that several cities claimed him as a native is testament to the lack of any firm biographical evidence, as well as to the widespread popularity of the Homeric poems. In addition to the insubstantial evidence for Homer himself, the language and contents of the poems further complicate the mystery of their composition. The language of both the *Iliad* and the *Odyssey* is an artificial, poetic creation, a mixture of distinct dialects enhanced at times with purely poetic word forms. Though constructed from the spoken language of the ancient Greeks, this Homeric language was never employed as everyday idiom, but was developed by highly trained bards specifically for the purpose of poetic performance. The poetry adheres to a fixed metrical rhythm, the dactylic hexameter; each verse contains six units of equivalent length, a combination of dactyls (one long syllable followed by two short syllables) and spondees (two long syllables). Cordery's vibrant translation substitutes for this meter the iambic pentameter, which is much better suited to the stress accents of English. Linguistic analysis reveals that the language of the Homeric poems cannot be the invention of a single individual but must instead result from generations of continued development, spanning several centuries. It is the product not of a poet, but of a poetic tradition. Accordingly, we find this same poetic language, with roughly the same diction and dialect mixture, employed also in the works of

Hesiod and several hymns to the Olympian gods. This language developed in conjunction with developments in the spoken language of the Greeks, and as the spoken language shifted over time, the poetic language shifted with it. But because not all the newly developing forms of the spoken language fitted easily into the established metrical scheme of the poetry, obsolete forms were sometimes retained. Thus we find older and newer word forms side by side within the same works. The mixture of dialects in the poems perhaps results from a fusion of traditional poetic dictions originally cultivated independently in regions where distinct dialects were spoken. Even to audiences of the eighth and seventh centuries BC, the language would have sounded distinctly artistic and at times archaic.

Furthermore, this poetic language cannot have developed in written form. Not only the mixture of dialects and word forms, but also the highly formulaic nature of the composition strongly suggests oral development. Consider, for example, the familiar epithets. Achilles is repeatedly labeled "Peleus' son," "godlike," or "the fleetfoot hero," and ships are regularly "dark," "well-benched," or "hollow." Comprehensive analysis of the poem reveals surprisingly systematic usage of such epithets. For each of several familiar nouns and names, the poet employs a limited number of epithet-noun combinations, each with a distinct metrical shape. The number of epithets available for each noun is large enough to fit a variety of metrical needs, but not so large as to burden the poet with broad choice. Thus we may infer that these epithet-noun combinations, while adding solemnity and dignity to the language, also functioned as tools of the oral poet, blocks of words that fitted conveniently into the metrical verse and thereby facilitated rapid improvisation. In addition to noun-epithet combinations, the poetry contains an abundance of other formulaic elements, including largely formulaic scenes such as the descriptions of arming and of sacrifice. Combining these formulaic tools with a gift for invention, a virtuoso performer would have been able to improvise a complex narrative poem while actually performing it, without the aid of writing or memorization of a script. And given

When Patroclus was killed, Achilles' grief was overwhelming, and he organized a huge funeral to honor the death of his dearest friend. A whole book of the poem is devoted to the description of the funeral and its rites; Patroclus' body was burned on a huge pyre, and Achilles sacrificed horses, dogs, and twelve Trojan prisoners of war with him.

the likely tendency of the bards to alter and enhance their stories in subsequent retellings, every new performance would have been unique. Thus the *Odyssey's* depiction of the blind bard Demodocus who sings tales of the Trojan War by request is not entirely implausible. Whether in fact a poem so long and complex as the *Iliad* could once have existed in a purely oral form, without a written text, and when it was first recited or first recorded are among the most controversial questions of classical scholarship. How many bards and how many generations shaped the tale of Achilles' wrath before it reached the form in which we now read it? Did one virtuoso performer living around 700 BC dictate while scribes recorded? Did a single gifted bard named Homer learn to write in order to embellish and record his masterpiece for posterity?

An equally intriguing mystery surrounds the origins of the myths featured in the Homeric poems. The excavation of impressive city ruins at Troy, Mycenae, and Knossos in the late nineteenth and early twentieth centuries gave hope to readers who insisted that historical events lay behind the mythology. Archaeological discoveries have revealed that complex civilizations with monumental architecture and exquisite artwork flourished in Greece during the second millennium BC, specifically the Minoan civilization centered in Crete, and the Mycenaean civilization that arose on the Greek mainland. And decipherment of the Linear-B script has confirmed that the Mycenaeans spoke a form of Greek. However, while some memory of these Bronze Age civilizations certainly survived through the Dark Ages of economic collapse around the close of the second millennium, connections between the Bronze Age and classical Greece are often tenuous. A few noteworthy weapons described in the *Iliad*, Ajax's towerlike shield *(Book 7)* and the helmet of boars' teeth worn by Odysseus *(Book 10)*, are reminiscent of Bronze Age artifacts, but many of the poem's details reflect more closely the Greek world of the eighth and seventh centuries. The name Hector has surfaced in Linear-B tablets, but here it apparently belongs to an ordinary Greek man, not a Trojan prince. The great flexibility of mythic traditions and the observed tendency of classical poets to elaborate, embellish, and romanticize inherited myths make scholars wary of treating the *Iliad* as a historical source. No doubt there were alliances among the various Mycenaean cities, and armies did besiege and sack cities in the Bronze Age. Strategically positioned near the entrance to the Hellespont, Troy may even have been an object of Greek attacks. But that Greeks and Trojans fought a war because a Trojan prince named Paris abducted the wife of a Spartan king named Menelaus simply cannot be verified. Rather than preserving an accurate record of historical events, Greek myth typically fills historical voids with imaginative legends, some of which may have originated in the Bronze Age, while others certainly

The aegis of Zeus was a terrifying instrument of war, brought in to play at various points in the poem by Athena, Apollo, and Zeus himself. It glared and shone with horrible brightness and, when shaken, unleashed a thunderous roar. Adversaries quailed before it, unmanned. Sometimes, Athena, the goddess of war, wore it as a breastplate; it was at once a real object and a symbol of the noise and confusion of war.

developed during the ensuing Dark Ages and the classical period. In fact, like numerous other contemporary Greek myths, the tale told of Achilles in the *Iliad* appears to originate not in Mycenaean history, but in Near-Eastern mythology. Achilles' inconsolable grief over the death of his dearest friend Patroclus finds a striking parallel in the legends of the Mesopotamian hero Gilgamesh and his beloved companion Enkidu. Paradoxically, while commonly viewed as a starting point for the Western literary tradition, the *Iliad* itself borrows from even more ancient poetic traditions.

Readers wishing to learn more about Greek mythology will find the major myths conveniently narrated in Richard Martin's *Myths of the Ancient Greeks* (2003). *Classical Mythology: Images and Insights* (2004), by Stephen L. Harris and Gloria Platzner, is one among several excellent college-level textbooks. For further study of the *Iliad*, Mark Edwards' *Homer: Poet of the Iliad* (1987) provides a comprehensive introduction to major critical issues and a commentary on selected portions of the poem. In addition to the present volume, several complete English translations of the poem are widely available: Richmond Lattimore's translation is extremely faithful to the wording of the original, Robert Fitzgerald's version adheres less closely to Homer's wording but conveys the sense and the power of the original well, and Robert Fagles' translation neatly balances fidelity and poetic license.

Zeus the charioteer; despite being a god who can manifest himself in any shape he likes, in the Iliad *Zeus often chose to ride like a mortal warrior in his golden chariot.*

MAP OF GREEK AND TROJAN ARMIES

GREEKS | TROJANS

ACAMAS (*Thracian commander*)
PEIROUS (*Thracian*)
RHESUS (*Thracian*)

EUPHEMUS
(*Ciconian leader*)

PANDARUS (*Leader of Trojan forces from Zeleia*)

ASCANIUS (*Phrygian leader from Ascania*)

ASCALAPHUS (*Illyrian commander*)

ILLYRIA

ASIUS
(*Commander of Trojan allies from Percote*)
ADRASTUS

DEIPHOBUS
(*Son of Priam*)

HECTOR (*Trojan commander-in-chief*)
PARIS (*Trojan commander*)

THRACE

Percote   Zeleia

ACHILLES
(*Myrmidon commander*)
PISANDER
(*Myrmidon commander*)

Mt Olympus

Hellespont   Dardanus
•TROY
DARDANIA
PHRYGIA

AENEAS (*Dardanian leader*)
ACAMAS (*Dardanian leader*)

POLYPOETES (*Lapith commander*)
LEONTEUS (*Lapith commander*)

Lemnos

Tenedos   TROAD   ▲ Mt Ida

MEGES
(*Achaean commander*)

MACHAON (*Thessalian commander*)
EUMELUS (*Thessalian commander*)
PHILOCTETES (*Thessalian commander*)
EURYPYLUS (*Thessalian commander*)
MEDON (*Thessalian commander*)

ANTIPHUS (*Maeonian commander*)

THESSALY   Pherae
Methone
Iolcus

ODYSSEUS
(*King of Ithaca*)

Aegean Sea

MYSIA

LITTLE AJAX
(*Locrian commander*)

Scyros

NEOPTOLEMUS (*Son of Achilles*)

LOCRIS
AETOLIA

SCHEDIUS (*Phocian commander*)

ITHACA

▲ Mt Parnassus
Delphi •   PHOCIS

ELEPHENOR
(*Commander of the Abantes*)

LYDIA

CEPHALLENIA

Aulis •
BOEOTIA

EUBOEA

MAEONIA

ACHAEA

THOAS (*Aetolian commander*)

• Buprasium
• Elis

Sicyon •

PENELEUS (*Boeotian commander*)
PROTHOENOR (*Boeotian commander*)
CLONIUS (*Boeotian captain*)

GLAUCUS (*Lycian commander*)
SARPEDON (*Lycian commander*)

•Mycenae
ARCADIA   Argos• •Tiryns •Epidaurus
ARGOLIS

Salamis   • Athens

MENESTHEUS (*Athenian commander*)

AMPHIMACHUS
(*Epean commander*)

MESSANIA

AJAX (*Salamis commander*)
TEUCER (*master archer*)

CARIA   LYCIA

Ionian
Sea

Pylos •

AGAMEMNON (*King of Mycenae and supreme commander of all Achaean forces*)

Cos

•Sparta
LACONIA

EURYPYLUS
(*King of Cos*)

Syme

NESTOR
(*King of Pylos*)
ANTILOCHUS
(*Nestor's son*)
THRASYMEDES
(*Nestor's son*)

ADRASTUS (*King of Sicyon*)

RHODES

MENELAUS
(*King of Sparta*)

DIOMEDES (*King of Argos*)
EURYALUS (*Argive commander*)

TLEPOLEMUS
(*Rhodian commander*)

Cretan Sea

IDOMENEUS (*King of Crete*)
MERIONES (*Cretan commander*)

CRETE

The Greek and Trojan armies were made up of factions from different regions, the
arrows point from the main cities and regions and show the leaders who held
them. The dotted line indicates the gods' direct view of Troy from Mount Olympus.

WHO'S WHO

Greeks, Trojans, and Gods

Menelaus, the wronged husband of Helen. After he failed to retrieve his wife, his brother Agamemnon led the Greek forces to Troy, to avenge the honor of the house of Atreus.

GREEKS

Achilles The flawed hero of the *Iliad*, the son of King Peleus (which is why he is described in the verse as Pelides, or son of Peleus) and the sea nymph Thetis, and the leader of the elite warriors known as the Myrmidons. He is the favorite of the goddesses Hera and Athena, and he particularly loves Patroclus.

Agamemnon The Greek leader and king of Mycenae, ruthless enough to sacrifice his own daughter to assure favorable winds for the fleet. He appears in the verse sometimes as Atrides, which means son of Atreus.

Ajax Son of Telamon (Great Ajax): Greek warrior from Salamis, second only to Achilles in his bravery and strength.

Ajax Son of Oïleus (Little Ajax): Greek warrior from Locris, short and wiry, and a brilliant wielder of the spear.

Antilochus The warrior son of Nestor.

Automedon The charioteer of Achilles.

Briseis Taken captive by Achilles but removed from him by Agamemnon, with serious consequences.

Calchas The chief seer of the Greek expedition, who has foretold how long the war will last and will eventually advise them to build a wooden horse.

Chryseis Daughter of the priest of Apollo, Chryses; captured by Achilles and given to Agamemnon—causing Apollo to send a plague to the Greek camp.

Clytemnestra Helen's half-sister and Agamemnon's wife. While Agamemnon is away, she has an affair with his cousin.

Diomedes Son of Tydeus (which is why he appears in the verse as Tydides, or son of Tydeus). He is the king of Argos, and one of the bravest of the Greeks after Achilles.

Euryalus One of the three commanders of the Peloponnesian force of 80 ships that go to Troy.

Eurybates Agamemnon's herald.

Eurypylus Comes from Ormenion with 40 ships.

Idomeneus The king of Crete and one of the bravest Greek warriors.

Machaon Son of Asclepius, a healer and surgeon who also fights and is wounded on the battlefield.

Meges One of Helen's suitors, who eventually leads his men from Dulichium and the Echinean islands against the Trojans.

Menelaus King of Sparta and red-haired younger brother of Agamemnon, supported by Hera and Athena in battle. He appears in the verse sometimes as Atrides, which means son of Atreus.

Meriones Joint leader of the Cretans, with Idomeneus.

Nestor The wise, old, voluble king of Pylos; counsellor to Agamemnon.

Neoptolemus Son of Achilles, brought to the war by Odysseus because of a prophecy that he was crucial to the capture of Troy. He is one of the warriors in the wooden horse, and was to kill King Priam and fling Astyanax over the walls of the city.

Odysseus The wily king of Ithaca, a wise negotiator.

Patroclus Greek warrior, loved by Achilles.

Peleus Father of Achilles and king of the Myrmidons: too old to take part in the war.

Teucer The best archer in the Greek army, son of Telamon and half-brother of Ajax.

TROJANS

Aeneas The son of Anchises and Aphrodite, leader of the Dardanians, and second only to Hector on the Trojan side.

Anchises The father of Aeneas, and loved by Aphrodite.

Andromache The wife of Hector and daughter of the king of Thebes, a city near Troy.

Antenor Trojan elder who advises the city to return Helen to the Greeks.

Astyanax Hector's little son.

Cassandra Priam's daughter, loved by Apollo, who gave her the gift of prophecy but, as a punishment, fated her never to be believed.

Deiphobus Son of Priam, who would marry Helen after the death of Paris.

Dolon Trojan spy.

Euphorbus Warrior son of Panthous.

Glaucus Grandson of Bellerophon, a Lycian prince and ally of Priam's.

Hecabe Priam's second wife and the mother of, among others, Hector, Paris, Deiphobus, and Cassandra. Later taken as a slave by Odysseus.

Hector Priam's son and the hero and commander-in-chief of the Trojan forces.

Helen The daughter of Zeus and the most beautiful woman in the world. She was the wife of Menelaus until Paris carried her off, the original cause of the siege of Troy.

Helenus Like his sister Cassandra, he has second sight and predicts the fall of Troy. He later marries Hector's widow, Andromache.

Paris Priam's son, also called Alexander, a skillful archer who was brought up by shepherds. Athena and Hera loathe him for choosing Aphrodite in a beauty contest for goddesses. His theft of Helen starts the Trojan War.

Polydamas Brother of Euphorbus and Hector's warrior friend.

Polydorus A son of Priam.

Priam The elderly king of Troy and father of 50 sons, including Hector and Paris.

Sarpedon A Lycian prince, and the son of Zeus.

Paris, son of Priam; the handsome prince who abducted Helen from Sparta and took her to Troy to marry her. His sister Cassandra foretold that he would be the destruction of his own city.

Aphrodite, the goddess of passionate love, and the divine personification of the idea that all is fair in love and war. When Paris chose her as the fairest of the goddesses, she rewarded him with Helen, the most beautiful woman in the world, disregarding the fact that she was married to someone else. In the Iliad, Aphrodite came to the defense of her princely protégé by whisking him away from the fighting, to the disgust of his brother Hector.

THE GODS

The gods in the *Iliad* live on Mount Olympus, but they are ever-present in the action, persistently intervening on one side or the other, and endlessly partisan in the struggle outside the gates of Troy, often even disguising themselves to take a direct part in the fighting. Nearly all the participants in the action believe that most or all of their actions are already predetermined or under the control of the gods. The main gods in the *Iliad* are:

Aphrodite Goddess of beauty and love, and the daughter of Zeus. Long before the events of the *Iliad*, Paris had judged a beauty competition between Aphrodite, Hera, and Athena. He chose Aphrodite, which is why the others are so determinedly on the side of his opponents.

Apollo The archer god, responsible for prophecy, and the son of Zeus. In fact, Apollo is also responsible for the sun, for music, poetry and painting, for plowing, for both healing and plagues, and for animals. Also known as Phoebus ("the shining one"). He is a supporter of the Trojans.

Ares The furious, handsome, and cruel god of war, symbolized by a bloody spear.

Artemis Twin sister of Apollo, and the goddess of the chase; she supports the Trojan side, but to no great effect.

Athena Goddess of wisdom, handicrafts, and war, the daughter of Zeus and passionately on the Greek side—especially the wise Odysseus. Often depicted together with her symbol, an owl.

Cronos One of the original Titans, who overthrew the rule of his father Uranus, and was in turn deposed by his own son Zeus.

Eris Goddess of strife; it is Eris who supplies the golden apple inscribed "For the Fairest" at the wedding of Thetis and Peleus, sparking off the deadly rivalry between Hera, Athena, and Aphrodite.

Eros The god of love, desire, and fertility; according to legend, it was Eros who first arranged the marriage between Uranus (the sky) and Gaia (earth).

Furies Harsh deities of justice, born from the blood of Uranus, the father of Cronos. They punish anyone who transgresses natural law, particularly anyone who fails to honor his or her parents.

Graces The handmaidens of Aphrodite, they gave refinement, joy, and gentleness, and inspired poetry.

Hades The god of the Underworld—the realm of the dead—and brother of Zeus and Poseidon, who were given the earth and the sea to rule.

Hebe Goddess of youth and daughter of Zeus.

Hephaestus Son of Hera, born lame and flung down from Olympus by his mother, returning there later as the craftsman and blacksmith of the gods.

Hera The jealous and irritable sister and consort of Zeus as Queen of Olympus, committed to supporting the Greeks. Also known as Herè.

Hermes Son of Zeus, messenger of the gods and the god of luck. It is the job of Hermes—often depicted with winged feet—to guide the dead to the Underworld, but he is also a great assistant to mankind, including Priam, especially when they are engaged on difficult quests.

Iris Messenger of the gods, mostly used by Zeus in the *Iliad*.

Poseidon God of the sea and brother of Zeus; he hated the Trojans for failing to pay him for helping them build their city walls.

Rhea The mother of Zeus, as well as of Poseidon and Hades.

Thetis A sea nymph, and mother of Achilles.

Zeus The king of the gods, ruling the universe from his home on Olympus. He was the youngest son of the Titans Cronos and Rhea. When he was born, his father Cronos intended to swallow him, as he had all of Zeus' siblings, but Rhea tricked Cronos and hid the infant Zeus in a cave in Crete. When he had grown up, Zeus made Cronos vomit up his sisters and brothers, and they joined together to seize control of the universe. He and his brothers, Poseidon and Hades, then divided up creation between them.

A BRIEF GLOSSARY

Achaea Homer never used the word "Greek"—he referred to Achaeans, a group of Greeks who inhabited Thessaly and parts of the Peloponnese.

Argives People from Argos. Homer used this as another term for Achaeans.

Danaans Another name used by Homer to refer to the Achaeans.

Dardania The land next to Troy, from the highlands of Asia Minor. The Dardanians were allies of the Trojans and under the command of Aeneas.

Hecatomb A sacrifice to the gods of 100 cattle.

Hellespont The narrow strait that connects the Aegean Sea with the Sea of Marmara.

Ida Mountain in Asia Minor, from where the gods watched over the battles outside Troy.

Ilium Another name for Troy: hence the *Iliad*, a poem about Ilium.

Lycia Mountainous country in Asia Minor, allied to Troy.

Mycenae Agamemnon's capital city.

Myrmidons From Thessaly in Greece, the elite troops commanded by Achilles.

Olympus The highest mountain in Greece and the home of the gods.

Pylians Inhabitants of Pylos, the home of Nestor, led in battle on the Greek side by Antilochus.

Tripod Ornate cauldron on three legs, often used in sacred rituals; usually considered a rich prize.

Xanthus The Trojan river, rising from two springs near Mount Ida, one warm and one freezing cold. Also known as the Scamander.

Armor and the description of armor was very important in the Iliad; *whenever a fighter fell, his armor was heard ringing about him, as the chain links clash together; and whenever a warrior killed another, it was customary to strip the armor— sometimes made of gold— from the corpse and take it as plunder. Many soldiers were themselves killed while trying to claim their loot.*

How It All Began

When the *Iliad* begins, the war between the Greeks and the Trojans has been raging for ten years—but what caused it? Two elements combined to set it in motion: the force of destiny, as guided by the gods; and a failure of diplomacy by the mortals. The trigger for the war was the elopement of Helen, the wife of Menelaus, king of Sparta, with Paris, a prince of Troy. When Menelaus failed to get his wife back by appealing to the Trojans' better nature, a huge host of Greek allies, led by Agamemnon, Menelaus' brother, descended on the city to regain Helen by force.

PARIS AND HELEN

Paris, also known as Alexander, was the son of Priam, king of Troy, and Hecabe. Just before he was born, his mother dreamed that she was going to give birth to a flaming torch, and it was foretold—possibly by Cassandra, Priam's prophetess daughter—that the child would bring destruction on the city. So the newborn baby was abandoned on a hillside outside Troy and left for dead. However, he was given milk by a she-bear, and found by shepherds who raised him as their own. When he had grown into a young man, Paris went to Troy to try his luck at the festival games there; Cassandra recognized him, and he was reinstated into the royal family. However, he continued to work as a shepherd, looking after Priam's flocks on the slopes of Mount Ida.

Helen was the daughter of the god Zeus and Leda, but was raised by Leda and her husband, Tyndareus, king of Sparta. Her sister was Clytemnestra and her brothers Castor and Polydeuces. Helen was stunningly beautiful, and when she reached an age to marry, she was so besieged by suitors (including Menelaus, Odysseus, Philoctetes, and both Ajaxes) that her mortal father worried that those who were refused would cause trouble. So, at the suggestion of Odysseus, Tyndareus made everybody swear to protect and defend whoever Helen finally chose to marry. Menelaus was the lucky man. His brother Agamemnon was already married to Helen's sister Clytemnestra.

THE JUDGMENT OF PARIS

When Peleus and Thetis, Achilles' parents, got married, Zeus himself presided over the festivities. Eris, the goddess of strife, had not been invited to the wedding, but she sneaked in, carrying a golden apple inscribed with the words "For the Fairest." She rolled the apple at the feet of Olympus' three great goddesses: Zeus' wife Hera, and Athena and Aphrodite, his daughters. They asked Zeus to choose which of them was the fairest, but he sensibly declined, and asked the handsome Paris, tending his flocks nearby, to make the choice instead. Each goddess offered seductive bribes. Aphrodite, understanding young men very well, promised him the most beautiful woman in the world; and so, to the bitter chagrin of Hera and Athena, Paris gave her the prize.

A few years later, Priam sent Paris on a diplomatic mission to Sparta. Menelaus had to leave to arrange the funeral of his Cretan grandfather; and Paris, realizing that Helen was the woman Aphrodite had promised him, seduced her and persuaded her to run away with him. The lovers fled, taking most of Menelaus' treasury with them. Some stories say they sailed straight to Troy, where they married, others that they traveled first to Sidon, Cyprus (Aphrodite's island), and Egypt.

THE OATHTAKERS' REVENGE

When Menelaus found Helen gone, he called on all those who had taken the oath to defend and protect him as Helen's chosen husband. He went to Troy with Odysseus, but failed to persuade the Trojans to give her up, so his brother Agamemnon assembled a huge fleet at Aulis, in Boeotia, with contingents from all the oathtakers and other allies. However, the fleet could not set sail because the wind was against them. Most stories claim that the wind was sent by the goddess Artemis, who felt slighted by Agamemnon; she demanded the sacrifice of his daughter Iphigenia. Intent on getting Helen back and restoring the honor of Sparta, Agamemnon lured Iphigenia to Aulis, promising her that she was to be the bride of Achilles. (Homer does not mention this sacrifice in the *Iliad*; Agamemnon offers all three of his daughters to Achilles to bribe him to return to battle.) Most versions of the story say that the girl was indeed sacrificed by her own father, and that her mother never forgave him; others maintain that Artemis substituted a young deer for the girl, whom she spirited away to be her priestess at Tauris. Whatever happened, the sacrifice worked, the gods sent favorable winds, and the fleet of over 1,000 ships set sail.

En route, Agamemnon decided to make a sacrifice to Apollo on the island of Chryse. Here, a fateful thing happened, which would affect the course of the war. The great archer Philoctetes, who had inherited the mighty bow of Heracles, was bitten by a snake; his wound festered and stank, and he screamed in pain constantly, so Odysseus proposed that they abandon him on the isle of Lemnos. This heartless decision would prolong the war—Helenus, a seer of Troy, prophesied that the city would not be taken until Philoctetes came to fight with Heracles' weapon, because he was destined to kill Paris. And so when the Greeks landed on the beach by Troy, their strategy was already compromised—their actions on Chryse would cause their campaign to last for ten long years.

CASSANDRA

CASSANDRA WAS THE DAUGHTER OF PRIAM AND HECABE, TWIN TO HELENUS. LIKE HIM SHE RECEIVED THE GIFT OF PROPHECY FROM APOLLO, BUT OFFENDED THE GOD, AND SO NONE OF HER PROPHECIES (ALL OF THEM ACCURATE) WERE BELIEVED. WHEN TROY FELL, SHE WAS GIVEN AS A PRIZE TO AGAMEMNON.

Book 1
THE RAGE OF ACHILLES

Achilles, Agamemnon, and Apollo

INSTANT *ILIAD*

IT IS THE TENTH YEAR
OF THE SIEGE OF TROY.
THE GREEK ARMY IS
BESET BY A GOD-SENT
PLAGUE, ACHILLES
AND AGAMEMNON
QUARREL OVER THE
SPOILS OF WAR, AND
ACHILLES' MONSTROUS
RAGE THREATENS TO
BRING THE GREEKS
TO THEIR KNEES.

In the Greek camp, on the beach below the besieged city of Troy, men were being slaughtered; not in battle, but by the plague-laden arrows of the god Apollo. Why? Because Agamemnon, the king of Mycenae and chief leader of the Greek forces, had abducted Chryseis, the daughter of Chryses. Chryses was the priest of Apollo, and he had come to Agamemnon to offer ransom for his daughter, and to ask for her return out of respect for the god (who was on the side of the Trojans). The entire Greek army had beseeched Agamemnon to give the girl up, but in his arrogance he had refused, and had sent the old priest away with threats and abuse. Chryses begged Apollo to intercede:

> *Hear me, O Bender of the Silver Bow,*
> *Who dwellst in Chrysa, or the fruitful dales*
> *Of Cylla, or in Tenedos enthroned,*
> *Sminthian Apollo! If that e'er I wreath'd*
> *About thy fragrant altar crowns of flowers,*
> *Or e'er have made to thee sweet sacrifice*
> *Of bulls and goats, fulfil me my desire:*
> *Venge with thy darts these tears upon their host.*

Apollo answered Chryses' prayer, with a vengeance. Now the Greek soldiers were dying like flies and the stench of decay and burning corpses filled the camp.

After nine days of this, Achilles, captain of the Myrmidons, was prompted by Hera, queen of Olympus, to call everyone together to find out why it was happening. Calchas the seer claimed to know the answer, but demanded protection from

Agamemnon's wrath before he would speak. When his safety was guaranteed, Calchas explained that Apollo was enraged because Agamemnon had treated his priest so badly; the god wanted the priest's daughter to be returned, and Agamemnon to sacrifice 100 bulls at Apollo's shrine.

Agamemnon leaped up, furious. He accused Calchas of doom-mongering— "Prophet of evil!"—and blazed that he wanted and deserved Chryseis:

> *... well thou know'st*
> *My longing to preserve her in my home;*
> *O'er Clytemnestra even, my wedded wife,*
> *I hold her; for to her in form and face*
> *And mind and needle-craft she*
> *   yields no whit.*

With a great show of forbearance Agamemnon then added that he would give Chryseis up, if it was absolutely necessary, as long as he was compensated with another prize, because it would be a disgrace for so great a leader as he to have no reward when everyone else did. Achilles retorted brusquely, saying it would be even more disgraceful to take plunder away from lower ranking soldiers who had won it fairly. He declared that Agamemnon should wait until more plunder was won, and take his reward then, when he could have double or triple the worth of the girl he had given up. Agamemnon was having none of this, and threatened to take a prize if no one would give him one—perhaps from Achilles himself:

> *If, indeed,*
> *The Achaians will surrender me a prize*
> *Equal in worth, as pleasing, in her stead—*
> *But if they will not, with mine own strong hand*
> *Thine I will seize, or from Odysseus his,*
> *Or Ajax his.*

Agamemnon abducted the daughter of Chryses, the priest of Apollo, as part of his war plunder. This was the act, an echo of Paris' abduction of Helen, that set off the action in the Iliad, and brought doom and disaster to Achilles and Agamemnon himself.

Achilles stood

breathing

hard, his

mind racing.

Outraged, Achilles glared darkly at Agamemnon, calling him shameless and mean-spirited. He pointed out that he and his men had no quarrel with Troy, and that they were only there to avenge the honor of Agamemnon's brother, Menelaus. He also complained that he never got his fair share of the booty anyway:

> *Yet never, when we take a town of Troy*
> *Do I receive as thou: albeit mine arm*
> *Doth more in perilous onset to and fro,*
> *Yet, in the parting of the spoil, thy lot*
> *Is still the larger.*

Achilles declared that he was going home. Agamemnon struck back, calling Achilles a disloyal deserter, and revealing during his rant the real reason for his hatred—that Achilles' warrior strength was a gift from the gods:

> *But thou—of heav'n-born kings I loathe thee most;*
> *Death and destruction dog thee at thy heels:*
> *Thy strength, thine only virtue—'tis from heav'n!*
> *Home then with all thy galleys and thy men,*
> *And lord it o'er the Myrmidonian crew,*
> *I reck not of thine anger!*

By now incandescent, Agamemnon swore to take Achilles' prize, the girl Briseis. Achilles stood breathing hard, his mind racing—should he swallow his fury, or unsheath his great sword and cut his tormentor down? Suddenly he felt a tugging on his hair, and turned to see the goddess Athena, her eyes blazing, at his back. He knew at once that she was visible only to him. She spoke, telling him she had been sent by Hera the white-armed queen, and promising great reward if he could master his rage:

> *From heav'n I come, Pelides,* and to stay*
> *Thine anger, if thou wilt be ruled of me—*
> *Sent by the Goddess of the milkwhite arm,*
> *Who loves you, each alike, with equal care.*
> *Hold therefore; cease this strife, nor draw thy sword;*
> *Rather reproach him with what soon shall be;*
> *For what I say shall surely come to pass;*

Ere long, gifts thrice her value shall be laid
Before thy feet in quittance of this wrong:
Hold thyself therefore and be ruled of us.

* *Pelides means son of Peleus, i.e. Achilles*

Achilles instantly sheathed his sword, bowing to the gods' commands, and the goddess went back to Olympus. But just because he had put away his weapon did not mean that Achilles had given up the fight. He rounded on Agamemnon, accusing him of being a drunk and a coward, claiming the rewards but never joining in the dangerous fighting. Then Achilles seized the scepter of authority and swore an oath, that he would never again come to Agamemnon's aid, not even in his darkest hour:

By this I swear—an oath to cost thee dear;
The day shall come when on Achaia's host
Shall fall a longing for Achilles' arm;
Then shalt thou curse thee that thou canst not save,
Whilst they fall slaughter'd under Hector's sword:
Then shall it rend thee to thy heart of hearts
Thou daredst upon their noblest this affront!

The two warriors glared at each other, angry and obstinate. Stalemate. Then Nestor, the wise elder statesman, spoke up, pleading with them to stop squabbling. He declared that they were just bringing comfort and joy to the enemy, wasting their energies with futile fighting among themselves. He pointed out, with respect, that better men than either of them had taken notice of his counsel before, and they would do well to listen to him. He begged Agamemnon not to take Briseis, Achilles' prize, just because he could, nor to antagonize the warrior who was the tower of strength that supported the Greek forces; then he implored Achilles not to rebel against his king because Zeus had conferred kingship upon him, and Achilles should respect Zeus' decisions.

Nestor could have saved his breath. Agamemnon and Achilles sat eyeball to eyeball, each shouting into the other's face. Agamemnon said that all Achilles wanted was to lead the army, and that he was not prepared to take orders from the rank and file, even if the gods had made him a great warrior. Achilles spat back that everyone would think he was a coward if he gave in, and that he would no longer take orders from him:

Go lord it over others; I obey
Thy word no more; nor thou, I trow, rul'st me!

APOLLO

THE SON OF ZEUS AND THE TITANESS LETO, APOLLO WAS TWIN TO ARTEMIS. HE WAS THE GOD OF DIVINATION, PROPHECY, MUSIC, AND ARCHERY, AND WAS ALSO KNOWN AS THE PLAGUE BRINGER. HE WAS SOMETIMES CALLED PHOEBUS, MEANING "BRIGHT SHINING ONE." THROUGHOUT THE TROJAN WAR HE STAUNCHLY SUPPORTED PRIAM AND TROY, CONFERRING THE GIFT OF PROPHECY ON TWO OF PRIAM'S CHILDREN, HELENUS AND CASSANDRA. IT WAS APOLLO'S ARROW THAT FINALLY KILLED ACHILLES, ALTHOUGH PARIS DREW THE BOW.

THETIS

THE SEA NYMPH THETIS
WAS THE DAUGHTER
OF NEREUS, AN
ANCIENT SEA GOD,
BUT WAS RAISED BY
HERA. SHE EARNED
ZEUS' LOVE BY
WARNING HIM OF A
PLOT BY HER FOSTER-
MOTHER TO REVOLT
AGAINST HIM. ZEUS
WANTED TO MARRY
THETIS, BUT IT WAS
FORETOLD THAT SHE
WOULD BEAR A SON
WHO WOULD BE
GREATER THAN HIS
FATHER, SO HE
MARRIED HER OFF TO
PELEUS, A MORTAL
KING. ACHILLES WAS
HIS SON. THETIS STILL
HAD GREAT INFLUENCE
WITH ZEUS AND
PERSUADED HIM TO
INTERVENE IN THE
TROJAN WAR TO
AVENGE ACHILLES'
HONOR.

> *Yet hear, and lay this warning to thy heart:*
> *Who gave may take away; and for the maid*
> *Ye gave me, I will raise no finger up*
> *Neither at thee nor any other man;*
> *But of all else aboard my swift black bark*
> *I dare thee to take aught at all away,*
> *Save at mine own good pleasure! If thou durst*
> *Attempt it, venture thither; and this host*
> *Shall know thee, when thy blood streams down my spear!*

So the two men parted company. Achilles stormed off to his camp with his comrade-in-arms Patroclus and his men. Agamemnon set about getting the boat ready to take Chryseis back to her father, sending Odysseus as his ambassador and captain of the ship.

Agamemnon wasted no time getting a replacement for his lost prize. While his troops were sacrificing bulls and goats to Apollo to make up for his folly, he sent his heralds, Talthybius and Eurybates, to Achilles' tent to take Briseis, his prize, from him, by force if necessary. They did not want to go, for they loved and respected Achilles, and they were frightened; they stood in silence before him, not daring to speak. But Achilles understood their silence, and told them not to be afraid:

> *Hail, heralds, messengers of Zeus and men!*
> *Draw nearer; for I blame not you, but him*
> *Who sent you, Agamemnon, and commands*
> *To take the maid Briseis; therefore haste,*
> *Noble Patroclus, bring the maiden forth*
> *And yield her to their hands.*

Achilles and Thetis

As Briseis was being taken to Agamemnon, Achilles slipped away, walked along the beach, and sat down wearily. He scanned the wide, gray ocean, thinking of his mother Thetis, a sea nymph, crying out to her in his misery and frustration.

His mother heard him, and rose from the depths. She took him in her arms and asked what was wrong. Achilles told her how Agamemnon had dishonored Apollo, and what Apollo had done to punish the Greeks, and how Agamemnon had returned

Chryseis but had then stolen Achilles' rightful reward. Achilles begged Thetis to talk to Zeus—who had always been fond of her—to persuade him to favor the Trojans, and make Agamemnon curse the day he had taken Achilles' prize:

> *Go therefore, seat thee near him, call thy deeds*
> *Back to his mind, and suppliant clasp his knees;*
> *So haply may he grant his aid to Troy,*
> *Conquering th' Achaians, shut against the sea,*
> *Back to their galley's sterns repell'd, and slain ...*

Thetis began to weep, lamenting the day she gave birth to Achilles, knowing that he was to have a short life, and now finding that it was to be filled with shame and misery. Wiping her eyes, she promised to go to Zeus with Achilles' request, but explained that he would have to wait another twelve days as Zeus and the other Olympians had gone to a feast with the Ethiopians. She advised Achilles to sit tight in his tent, keep his anger against Agamemnon stoked up, but not to fight in any battles. Then she disappeared back into the ocean, leaving Achilles still inconsolable.

She advised Achilles to sit tight in his tent, and keep his anger against Agamemnon stoked up.

Achilles, the Greeks' hero, whose obdurate rage against Agamemnon took him away from the fighting until the death of Patroclus inspired him to go to war.

Meanwhile, Odysseus had reached the island of Chryses. The ship was safely anchored and a hundred cattle—the hecatomb—destined for sacrifice were led off. The cattle were ranged in a circle around the altar, where their throats were cut and their skins flayed. Meat was cut from the thighs, and the thighbones were double wrapped in fat and bound with strips of meat. These were the sacrificial portions, and Chryses poured wine over them as they burned on the sacred fire. Then the rest of the meat was cut up and strung on pronged forks to roast for the feast. Wine was drunk (the first cup always being poured on the ground in honor of the god) and songs sung in praise of Apollo. At dawn the next day the god provided a favorable wind, and Odysseus and his men sailed back to the Greek encampment. The Greeks were relieved that the plague had gone, but Achilles sat alone and angry by his ships, longing for the glory of war yet refusing to fight.

CATTLE SACRIFICE

SACRIFICE TO THE GODS WAS ESSENTIAL TO GAIN THEIR FAVOR FOR AN ENTERPRISE OR PLACATE THEM IF THEY WERE ANGRY. THE BEASTS HAD THEIR THROATS CUT OVER AN ALTAR AND A CHOICE PIECE OF MEAT WAS PREPARED FOR THE GOD TO WHOM THE SACRIFICE WAS MADE. THIS PORTION WAS BURNED OVER THE FIRES SO THAT THE SMOKE AND SAVOR OF THE MEAT COULD RISE TO THE GOD'S HOUSE, AND WINE WAS POURED OVER IT IN LIBATION. THE REST OF THE CARCASS WAS CUT UP AND SPIT-ROASTED FOR A FEAST.

Trouble on Olympus

After twelve days, the gods returned from Ethiopia and Thetis kept her promise to Achilles. She went up to Olympus where she found Zeus alone on the very highest peak. She knelt before him, clasping his knees, and prayed:

> *My father, oh if ever amongst the Gods*
> *I gave delight to thee by deed or word,*
> *Fulfil me my desire, and glorify*
> *My son; to whom, though doom'd to early death,*
> *Yet hath Atrides Agamemnon dealt*
> *Foul outrage, plundering of his meed beloved.*
> *Therefore, great Zeus, put thou thy wisdom forth;*
> *Vouchsafe him glory; and so long to Troy*
> *Suffer the triumph, till the Achaians make*
> *Atonement by full honor and by gifts.*

Zeus sat in silence; he sat so long in silence that Thetis had to ask again:

> *Promise me true; confirm it by thy Nod;*
> *Or else deny me; what hast thou to fear?*

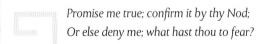

Zeus finally spoke. He was troubled. Thetis had asked him to promise something he knew would enrage Hera, who had already accused him, in full view of all the other gods, of siding with Troy. He was also worried that Hera would see him conversing with Thetis and become even more angry. Nevertheless he promised Thetis that he would do as she asked. Satisfied, Thetis returned to her home in the depths of the ocean, and Zeus descended to his palace on the slopes of Olympus. As he strode toward his throne, the other gods all stood up respectfully, but he did not fool Hera, who had seen him with Thetis. She immediately started complaining that Zeus was always plotting with other gods whenever her back was turned:

> *Say now, my crafty-hearted Lord, what God*
> *Hath communed of thy counsel? As of old,*
> *So now thou lov'st if I be e'er apart,*
> *To sit in secret judgment, nor to me,*
> *An thou hadst but thy wish, wouldst tell me one word.*

Zeus replied wearily that she was his wife and that if he thought she ought to know something he would tell her, and that she should stop poking and prying. Hera saw through this instantly and said that she was afraid that Zeus had promised to give victory to the Trojans to avenge Achilles. Of course she was right, but as Zeus then warned her angrily, there was not much she could do about it. He roared out in a rage that he was king of the gods and could destroy them at a stroke if he willed it so.

Hera sat in terrified silence after this outburst, and the rest of the gods shook in fear. Hephaestus, the smith god, tried to smooth things over between his mother and father, pointing out that it was ridiculous for two gods to come to blows over the trivial activities of mere mortals. Hephaestus pleaded with his mother Hera to do as Zeus commanded—the last time he had defended his mother, Zeus had taken him by the foot and hurled him out of Olympus:

> *Endure it, O my mother, nor be wroth;*
> *Lest, in my love's despite, before all heav'n*
> *I see thee ill-entreated, howsoe'er*
> *I sorrow'd, I could nought avail to help.*

Hera smiled at her son, gave in, and accepted a cup of wine from Hephaestus as did all the gods, and there was feasting and singing. Then the gods retired to their own splendid halls; and Zeus and Hera slept together on Zeus' own bed.

ZEUS

THE LORD OF THE SKY, AND KING OF THE GODS, ZEUS RULED FROM MOUNT OLYMPUS. THE SON OF RHEA AND CRONOS, ZEUS HAD BEEN RAISED IN SECRET ON THE ISLAND OF CRETE. WHEN HE CAME OF AGE, HE LED HIS BROTHERS AND SISTERS IN A REVOLT AGAINST HIS FATHER, AND OVERTHREW HIM. ZEUS CONSORTED WITH MANY NYMPHS, GODDESSES, AND MORTAL WOMEN, PRODUCING MANY CHILDREN, BUT HIS LASTING MARRIAGE WAS TO HERA. THUNDERBOLTS WERE HIS WEAPON OF CHOICE, AND HE HAD SUPREME POWER OVER GODS AND MORTALS ALIKE, WITH SPECIAL RESPONSIBILITY FOR MORTAL KINGS.

Book 2
THE ARMIES GATHER

Agamemnon's dream

Zeus decided to send an evil spirit in a dream to Agamemnon, urging him to seize the day and attack Troy at once. He knew that Agamemnon, the blind fool, would believe that Zeus was now on his side, not realizing that the dream was false:

> *Quick hence, thou Spirit of Evil! In false dream*
> *Pass through the fleet to Agamemnon's tent*
> *And there speak clearly, as I now give hest.*
> *Bid him throughout the camp to call to arms*
> *The streaming-hair'd Achaians, now at length*
> *To take broad-streeted Troy; for now no more*
> *Stand sunder'd in two bands the Olympian Powers;*
> *But Herè's prayer hath won them, and distress*
> *Hangs o'er the Trojans by the doom of Zeus.*

As Agamemnon lay sleeping in his tent, the evil dream sent by Zeus appeared to him in the shape of Nestor, the wise counselor. Claiming to be sent by Zeus, and using the god's own words, the phantom urged Agamemnon to muster his armies ready to attack immediately, then vanished. Agamemnon dreamed on of victory, little realizing that Zeus meant to bring death and destruction to both Greeks and Trojans.

At dawn, with the voice of the dream still echoing in his head, Agamemnon leaped up and, seizing the scepter of authority, strode out and ordered his heralds to signal all the troops to assemble. At the same time, he called together his trusted chiefs; they met beside Nestor's ship, where Agamemnon described his dream. Then he asked how they could best persuade all the different factions to come together for a main assault on Troy. He himself had a cunning plan—he would test the men by telling them to give up and go home as the cause was hopeless; Odysseus, Nestor, and the other chiefs could take up strategic positions round the camp and stop them leaving. There was a short silence, then Nestor stood up to speak, saying that they should follow Agamemnon's plan:

> *Friends, Chieftains, Captains of Achaia's host!*
> *Were he some other who declared this dream,*
> *Perchance we might denounce it false, and put*
> *The matter from us: but who tells the tale*
> *Is our liege lord. Rise therefore; in this wise*
> *Incite Achaia's sons to don their arms.*

Soldiers swarmed from their ships and tents, crowding along the broad beach, driven on by rumor and wild guesswork about what was going on. By the time that they had all reached the meeting ground and crammed themselves onto the benches, there was uproar; it took nine heralds, shouting at the tops of their lungs, to get them to be quiet. Eventually there was silence. Then Agamemnon stood before them, raising his scepter above his head, and delivered a speech the very opposite of rousing. He told the soldiers that Zeus had betrayed him and them and that he had been commanded to leave, empty-handed, despite the fact that many Greeks had died in this futile war. Even though the Greeks outnumbered the Trojans by ten to one, Agamemnon went on, the enemy had strong allies who had thwarted their battle plans at every turn. The Greeks had now been fighting for nine years and had gotten nowhere; their ships were rotting on their hawsers, and back home their families waited in vain for their return. It was all hopeless. They should follow his orders, and go home:

> *Hear, therefore, and obey as I advise.*
> *Let us away to our dear fatherland;*
> *Flee, for broad-streeted Troy shall ne'er be ours.*

Exactly what Agamemnon was hoping to achieve by this piece of reverse psychology was not clear; what he did achieve was panic. Fear, alarm, confusion, and despondency surged through the ranks, and together the men turned and ran to their ships, desperate to get away, give up the terrible war, and go home. They would have put to sea and gotten away too, flying against their true fate, if Hera had not been looking

AGAMEMNON

KING OF MYCENAE AND BROTHER TO MENELAUS, AND THEREFORE BROTHER-IN-LAW TO HELEN, AGAMEMNON WAS THE SUPREME COMMANDER OF ALL THE GREEK FORCES DURING THE WAR, AND LED THE LARGEST CONTINGENT OF 100 SHIPS. AS IT WAS HE WHO HAD PERSUADED KING TYNDAREUS, HELEN'S FATHER, TO GIVE HER TO MENELAUS, IT WAS A POINT OF HONOR FOR HIM TO HELP RESCUE HER FROM HER ABDUCTOR. SOME AUTHORITIES CLAIM THAT HE SACRIFICED HIS DAUGHTER IPHIGENIA, TO GAIN A FAVORABLE WIND TO GET THE GREEK FLEET TO TROY.

on from Olympus. Horrified, she called to Athena, the warrior goddess, commanding her to stop the ships from launching and persuade the Greeks not to give up:

> *Child of Great Zeus, and peerless Power of war!*
> *Say, shall the Argives to their fatherland*
> *Safe on the sea's broad shoulders take this flight,*
> *Leaving the boast to Priam and to Troy*
> *Of Argive Helen, for whose dear behoof*
> *Far from their fatherland so many have fall'n?*
> *Nay, haste thee rather to their mailèd host,*
> *And stay them, as thou mayst, with calming words,*
> *Nor suffer that their galleys reach the deep.*

Athena flew down from Olympus, straight to Odysseus, who stood in shock by his ship, aghast at the results of Agamemnon's "test." The goddess spoke to him, repeating Hera's words. He recognized her voice and suddenly he knew what to do. Flinging his cloak aside he ran through the throng until he found Agamemnon, snatched the scepter of authority from him, and strode toward the ships, intent on preventing the rout.

Every king or chief that Odysseus met he spoke to, man to man, expressing surprise at what appeared to be their cowardly behavior and putting the best spin he could on Agamemnon's speech—that it had been a plan, a test of their valor, that there was a purpose to it that the king wasn't ready to reveal. Fingering the scepter of authority in a meaningful manner, he added that he was afraid of the divine anger a king might let loose on an army that deserted him:

> *My friend, this cowardlike fear beseems not thee.*
> *Take seat thyself, and bid the people sit.*
> *Thou knows't not fully what the King's intent:*
> *We all were not in council when he spake:*
> *He tempts, but soon will sorely smite, the host:*
> *I dread his anger, lest he do them hurt;*
> *For heavy is the wrath of heavensprung kings,*
> *Honour'd of Zeus, of wisest Zeus beloved.*

Odysseus took a more direct method with the rank and file, beating them with the scepter to remind them who was in charge. So Odysseus, with the help of Athena, turned back the deserters and brought them all back to the meeting ground.

Calchas had prophesied that the Greeks would be victorious after nine years of war.

Rallying the troops

Still brandishing the scepter of authority, Odysseus stood before the Greek armies, Athena at his side disguised as a herald. His speech was addressed to Agamemnon, but it was designed to impress the troops. He said that they had behaved like weaklings, but that he could not blame them after nine years of spirit-sapping, unproductive war; yet it would be shameful and a dishonor to those already killed in battle to give up and leave empty-handed. He reminded them of the omen Zeus had given them at Aulis, years ago, when they had first gathered to sail for Troy. There had been a fearsome serpent that had eaten a nestful of newborn sparrows—eight fledglings—and their mother. From this omen, the seer Calchas had prophesied that the Greeks would be victorious after nine years of war; surely everyone wanted to find out if the prophecy would come true? Odysseus urged the soldiers to stick it out:

> *Wherefore, endure, brave warriors, still endure,*
> *Till Priam's haughty citadel be thrown.*

Odysseus sat down amid thunderous applause. Seizing the moment, Nestor stood up and added his own brand of fighting talk. He was disappointed in his audience. What had become of the solemn oaths they had sworn? The sacrificial wine poured so ceremoniously? The clenched handshakes? Now was the time to strike, after nine years of getting nowhere and who better to lead the armies into war than the mighty Agamemnon; and death to any deserters who were too scared to stay and see if Zeus would keep his word. Then he advised Agamemnon to marshal the troops in clans— that way he could see just who was the coward and who the loyal ally—and if they did fail to take Troy, at least it would be clear what was to blame, the will of the gods or human cowardice and military ineptitude.

Odysseus and Nestor had done their work well; when Agamemnon stood up to speak, the troops had been so fired up with expertly spun dreams of victory, glory, and a final end to war that they had forgotten his previous "orders" and were ready to follow him anywhere. This time, his speech was on the button: he humbly thanked Nestor for his advice, saying that if only there were a few more like him, Troy could have been taken years ago; he hinted that it was all Zeus' fault—the god had clouded his brain so that he had quarreled with Achilles over a trifle; and then, before any awkward questions could be asked, he urged the men to go back to their tents, pray to their gods, eat well, feed their horses, and get their war gear and chariots

AGAMEMNON'S SCEPTER

THE SCEPTER OF AUTHORITY THAT AGAMEMNON CARRIED WAS A SIGN OF HIS KINGSHIP, AND A SYMBOL OF HOW THAT KINGSHIP DERIVED FROM ZEUS HIMSELF. THIS IS WHAT GAVE AGAMEMNON HIS DIVINE RIGHT TO POWER. THE IVORY SCEPTER WAS MADE BY HEPHAESTUS, THE BLACKSMITH GOD, FOR ZEUS. ZEUS GAVE IT TO HERMES THE MESSENGER GOD; HERMES GAVE IT TO PELOPS, HALF-MORTAL SON OF KING TANTALUS AND THE GODDESS DIONE; AND PELOPS HAD GIVEN IT TO HIS SON ATREUS, THE FATHER OF AGAMEMNON. OTHER "SCEPTERS OF AUTHORITY," NOT DESCENDED FROM ZEUS, WERE ROUTINELY USED DURING ASSEMBLIES AND MEETINGS, WHEN HERALDS WOULD HAND THEM OUT TO WHOEVER WISHED TO SPEAK THEIR PIECE.

ready for the final onslaught. Naturally, the soldiers cheered him to the echo, and then dispersed to their tents to prepare for the attack.

Agamemnon called together his chiefs, Nestor, Idomeneus, Ajax, Diomedes, and Odysseus, and his brother, Menelaus. They sacrificed a fine, fat, mature bull to Zeus, and Agamemnon prayed:

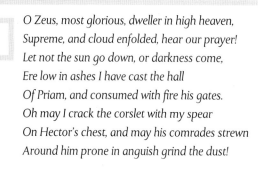

> *O Zeus, most glorious, dweller in high heaven,*
> *Supreme, and cloud enfolded, hear our prayer!*
> *Let not the sun go down, or darkness come,*
> *Ere low in ashes I have cast the hall*
> *Of Priam, and consumed with fire his gates.*
> *Oh may I crack the corslet with my spear*
> *On Hector's chest, and may his comrades strewn*
> *Around him prone in anguish grind the dust!*

Little did he know that Zeus, while accepting the sacrifice as his by right, had no intention of granting this prayer, but planned to inflict savagery on both sides.

Assembling the Greek fighting machine

When they had eaten, Nestor—perhaps suspecting that collective courage would ebb—urged Agamemnon to call the troops to arms, suggesting that he walk among the men himself to give encouragement and motivation. So Agamemnon and his chiefs walked through the ranks, and with them went Athena, holding aloft the aegis of Zeus; the very sight of the glorious golden shield inspired battle lust in all who saw it.

And so the warriors poured out of their tents and ships, spreading over the vast Xanthus plain before the walls of Troy like a great flock of birds landing, or a swarm of black flies covering a vast pail of new milk. And in the midst of it all towered Agamemnon, tall and powerful, made godlike by Zeus:

The Greek warriors wore helmets, chainmail body armor, and greaves to protect their legs, and fought with spears, swords, knives, and very often anything nearby, such as large rocks. How the rank and file fought is not described in the Iliad, *but the elite warriors were ferried around the battlefield in chariots.*

> *As 'mongst a herd the bull appears, of all*
> *Conspicuous, proud amid the grazing kine,*
> *Such Atreus' Son was shown of Zeus that day,*
> *Pre-eminent o'er heroes, and their king.*

THE GREEK ALLIES

THE GREEK FORCES CAME
FROM THE FOLLOWING
CITIES AND REGIONS:

AETOLIA
ARCADIA
ARGISSA
ARGOS
ASPLEDON
ATHENS
BOEOTIA
BUPRAISIUM
CALYDNA
CRETE
CYPHUS
DULICHION
EUBOEA
ITHACA
LOCRIS
MAGNESIA
METHONE
MYCENAE
ORMENION
PHERAE
PHOCIS
PHTHIA
PHYLACE
PYLOS
RHODES
SALAMIS
SPARTA
SYME
THESSALY
TIRYNS
TRICCA

It was impossible to say just how many men there were; there were more than 1,000 ships drawn up along the beach, and each contained as many as 120 men. There were contingents from Boeotia and Crete, Athens and Mycenae, Argos and Cephallenia; they came from the fertile mainland, from the mountains, from islands large and small, from great city states and from tiny kingdoms, each group led by a captain. All the heroes were there—Agamemnon, Menelaus, Odysseus, Idomeneus, Nestor, Diomedes, Philoctetes, Tlepolemus the son of Heracles, and the two Ajaxes; the only one of those present who did not join in the great muster was the greatest of them, Achilles; he skulked in his tent, while his men played aimless games and sports, or wandered moodily around their camp disconsolate, looking on enviously as the great host marched by them, shaking the earth with the tramp of their feet:

For none was peer
To great Achilles, nor could match his steeds.
But sullen now amongst his swift black barks
Anger'd with Agamemnon, Atreus' son,
He lay withdrawn; and on the indented shore
With play of quoit or javelin, or with bow,
His men disported; idly stood their steeds,
Each by his chariot cropping from the marsh
Lotos or parsley: or within their tents
His captains' cars lay empty; and themselves,
Lamenting their lost leader, through the camp
Roam'd listless to and fro, but went not forth.

Panic in Troy

Meanwhile, Zeus had decided to even up the odds. He sent Iris, his messenger, to Troy. She found the Trojan captains gathered anxiously around the city gates, Priam among them, holding a council of war. Disguised as Polites, one of Priam's sons, she delivered the words of Zeus, intended to stampede the Trojans into action:

> *Resistless comes the war.*
> *Oft have I enter'd battle, yet till now*
> *Such and so vast a host I ne'er beheld.*
> *Like leaves or sand for multitude, they come*
> *Across the plain to fight beneath our walls.*

Hector should muster his troops at once, and take overall command. Everyone believed what Iris told them, as the real Polites was the lookout man, perched on a high tomb that overlooked the beach and the Greek encampment. Hector, understanding immediately that the message came from the gods, wasted no time, breaking up the meeting and calling the Trojan army and all their allies, already in the city, to arms. Allied troops came from the nearby cities along the Hellespont and from as far away as Thrace and Paphlagonia, Caria and Lycia. With them came the heroes Aeneas, Pandarus, Acamas, Peirous, Ascanius, Sarpedon, and Glaucus. Hector flung open the gates of Troy and ranged his troops along the sharp, high ridge in front of the city.

And so the two armies confronted each other.

THE TROJAN ALLIANCE

THE TROJANS CALLED ALLIES FROM THE FOLLOWING CITIES AND REGIONS:

ABYDOS
ALYBE
ASCANIA
CARIA
CROMNA
DARDANIA
IDA
ISMAREOS
LARISSA
LYCIA
MAEONIA
MILETUS
MYSIA
PAEONIA
PAPHLAGONIA
PERCOTE
PHRYGIA
PITYEA
SESTOS
THRACE

Agamemnon had overall command of over 120,000 fighting men. They vastly outnumbered the forces of Troy, but the Trojans had the advantage of fighting on home ground, and having a well-defended town to retreat to when necessary.

Book 3
HELEN AND THE CHAMPIONS

The cowardice of Paris

INSTANT *ILIAD*

THE GREEK AND
TROJAN ARMIES MEET
OUTSIDE THE WALLS OF
TROY. PARIS MAKES
A GREAT DISPLAY BUT
IS FRIGHTENED OFF BY
MENELAUS. HECTOR,
HIS BROTHER, SHAMES
HIM INTO
CHALLENGING
MENELAUS TO A ONE-
ON-ONE FIGHT TO END
THE WAR; IF PARIS
WINS, THE GREEKS WILL
BE ALLOWED TO LEAVE
IN PEACE; IF MENELAUS
WINS, THE GREEKS WILL
TAKE HELEN BACK, PLUS
HANDSOME WAR
REPARATIONS. SOLDIERS
ON BOTH SIDES ARE
OVERJOYED THAT THE
WAR WILL SOON END;
BUT THE GODS,
ESPECIALLY APHRODITE,
HAVE OTHER IDEAS.

The armies marched grimly toward each other, clouds of dust swirling from their tramping feet. The Trojans advanced, banging their shields and screaming battle cries; the Greeks moved silently, hard-faced and implacable. As the front lines drew closer together, Paris suddenly leaped out of the Trojan ranks. Looking every inch the godlike warrior, he swaggered arrogantly up and down the lines, draped in leopard skin, his bow on his back, a sword at his hip, and a bronze-tipped spear in each hand. He challenged any of the Greeks who thought they were mighty enough to come and fight him.

When Menelaus saw him strutting around in front of the troops he could not believe his luck; he licked his lips like a hungry lion stumbling on a fresh kill—there he was, Paris, the wife-stealer, offering himself on a plate. Hot for revenge, Menelaus sprang down from his war chariot, fully armed and ready for action. At the sight of the fierce Spartan, Paris suddenly melted back into his own ranks, cringing with fear.

Paris' brother Hector was disgusted with him, and tore into him mercilessly. Paris was just a weak philanderer whose womanizing ways had gotten the Trojans into the war, and he was now making them a laughing stock:

> *Paris, thou curse! For women madman mere!*
> *So fair and false! Oh hads't thou died unborn*
> *Nor ever wedded—would 'twere so—yea, 'twere*
> *Better for thine own self, than thus to live*
> *The byword and foul proverb of the world!*
> *Hear'st thou that laugh?*

Hector was mortified that the Greeks now thought that Paris was the best champion Troy could field; the man was a curse to his father, his city, and his people, and a joy to his enemies. It was shameful that Paris would not face up to the anger of the man whose wife he had stolen. Paris may have sold himself to Aphrodite, but what use were her gifts—the pretty face and gorgeous hair—they did nothing to help him fight like a man. Hector was angry and ashamed of himself and his fellow Trojans—they had been weak, and should have stoned Paris to death years ago, and finished all this fighting.

Paris answered reasonably. He pointed out that Hector had a dauntless heart and so could not really understand how most people quailed before danger; and that no one should criticize gifts from the gods, for fear of reprisals. Then he redeemed himself by saying that he would fight man-to-man with Menelaus for Helen and an end to the war. Whoever won would leave the other side in peace:

Helen was Aphrodite's reward to Paris. He judged the goddess of love to be the fairest in a competition held at the marriage of Achilles' parents, because she had promised him the most beautiful woman in the world. Hera and Athena, the rejected goddesses, were so angry that they did everything in their power to see that Troy lost the war.

> *Howbeit, since thou wouldst have me battle thus,*
> *Bid all th' Achaians and the Trojans else*
> *Sit down, and in the centre, face to face,*
> *Plant me with Menelaus, there to fight*
> *For Helen and the booty ta'en withal.*
> *And, whoso conquering shows the better man,*
> *With her and with the booty let him go*
> *Unhinder'd home; but ye the rest swear truce*
> *Faithful o'er the victims slain, and all in peace*
> *Inhabit fruitful Troy; whilst they return*
> *To Argos and the pastures of their steeds,*
> *And the famed women of Achaia's land.*

Thrilled and relieved, Hector clapped his brother on the back; then he leaped into action and strode along the battle lines, holding his spear horizontally in front of him to show he meant no harm. Even so, some Greek archers had him in their sights, and other soldiers began pelting him with rocks, until Agamemnon shouted aloud to stop them. Silence fell, then Hector spoke, appealing to both sides. He outlined Paris' offer:

> *He bids all else*
> *Doff their bright arms and lay them on the earth,*
> *Whilst he with Menelaus in our midst*
> *Fights hand to hand for Helen and her wealth.*

More silence. Then Menelaus spoke. He agreed to the challenge, accepting that the war was all about his quarrel with Paris, and so it was only right that he should take responsibility for it. He was willing to fight to the death to end the war:

> *Likewise hear me; for deepest in my heart*
> *Hath this grief pierced. But now I hail the end,*
> *When, after all their suffering in my cause*
> *For Alexander's* wrong original,*
> *Troy and Achaia can be sunder'd free.*
> * Another name for Paris

Menelaus was a shrewd man, and wanted a watertight deal; he demanded an official, binding ceremony to seal the oath. He ordered that sacrificial lambs be brought—one from the Greeks for Zeus, two from Troy for Gaia, the Earth and Helios, the Sun—and that the Trojan king Priam should be present at the ritual. All parties would swear the oath to Zeus, but Menelaus considered Paris and Hector too impulsive and hot-headed to seal a serious oath; he wanted Priam to do it.

Both armies were jubilant, and thanked the gods that the war would end at last. They pulled up their chariots, took off their armor and, milling together, crowded around the combat zone, keen to see a fight.

HELEN

Helen hears the news

Meanwhile, a messenger came to Helen, who was keeping herself busy in her room, working on a blood-red robe that was woven with images of the battle being fought over her. Zeus had sent the goddess Iris, disguised as Laodice, Helen's sister-in-law. Iris whispered to Helen to come and see what was going on:

> *Come forth, dear Nymph, and view the godlike deeds*
> *Of mail'd Achaians and Troy's charioteers,*
> *Who each on other, scarce one moment past*
> *Brought tear-abounding Ares, and career'd*
> *Thirsting for slaughterous battle o'er the plain;*
> *But now sit silenced (and the strife is stay'd)*
> *Reclined upon their bucklers, with their spears*
> *Planted in the earth beside them. In their midst*
> *Paris and Menelaus, Atreus' son,*
> *Will meet in single battle match'd for thee;*
> *Who conquers, his dear wife shalt thou be named.*

Hearing Menelaus' name, Helen felt pangs of longing and regret for her old life with him and their only child, long ago in Sparta. Anxious to see the outcome of the contest, she wrapped herself in her long robe and ran weeping along the ramparts.

The old men of Troy, those whose fighting days were long over, were accustomed to sit above the ramparts in one of the gate towers, looking down on the battle. They were sitting there now, discussing the latest developments. Seeing Helen running, they shook their heads sadly, murmuring to each other, paying homage to her beauty, yet regretting its devastating effects on the sons of Troy:

HELEN WAS THE DAUGHTER OF ZEUS AND LEDA, WIFE OF TYNDAREUS, KING OF SPARTA. HELEN WAS STAGGERINGLY BEAUTIFUL. SO MANY SUITORS CLAMORED FOR HER HAND THAT TYNDAREUS, WORRIED THAT THE REJECTED LOVERS WOULD START TROUBLE, AND PROMPTED BY ODYSSEUS, WHO WAS ONE OF THEM, FORCED THEM TO SWEAR AN OATH: THEY WOULD ALL COME TO THE AID OF HELEN AND HER EVENTUAL HUSBAND IF EVER THEY NEEDED IT. MENELAUS WAS THE CHOSEN ONE. SO WHEN HELEN WAS TAKEN TO TROY, EVERY SUITOR WENT TO TROY TO FIGHT TO GET HER BACK.

No blame, no marvel, for such woman's sake
The hosts endure this suffering; for she seems
Like to Immortals—wondrous to behold.
Yet would, despite her beauty, she were gone,
And this dread trouble with her from our sons!

But kindly old King Priam called her to his side and tried to cheer her:

Draw near, mine own dear child, and seat thee here;
Whence thou mayst look down on thine olden lord,
Thy kith and kin and friends. For not to thee
I give the blame, but to the Powers of Heaven,
Of this dread quarrel and the woes of war.

Then, perhaps to take her mind off what was to come, Priam began to ask about all the mighty Greek warriors who stood on the plain before them, their names and their history. So Helen stumbled over her sorrow and began to answer Priam's questions, talking about Agamemnon king of Argos, the slippery Odysseus, Great Ajax the warrior, and the Cretan charioteer Idomeneus; and the old Trojan king had something courteous to say about every one of them.

The oath is sworn

Out on the battlefield, the lambs had been brought to slaughter; then the Greek heralds came to invite Priam to swear the oath of truce with Hector and Menelaus, and witness the battle of the champions:

Rise, Priam, son of great Laomedon!
For either's chieftains call thee to the plain
To strike the sacred pledges of their truce.
Then Paris hand to hand 'gainst Atreus' Son
Will fight with sharp-tipp'd lances for their wife.

Priam sighed. In his heart, he feared for his son Paris; nevertheless he ordered up his chariot and set off to meet the Greeks at the strip of no-man's-land where the combat

PARIS

PARIS WAS ONE OF PRIAM'S MANY SONS, DOOMED TO BE THE DESTRUCTION OF HIS CITY. AT THE WEDDING OF THETIS AND PELEUS, THE PARENTS OF ACHILLES, THE GODDESS OF STRIFE, ERIS, ROLLED A GOLDEN APPLE INSCRIBED "FOR THE FAIREST" AT THE FEET OF HERA, ATHENA, AND APHRODITE. ZEUS CALLED ON PARIS TO ADJUDICATE. HE CHOSE APHRODITE, AFTER SHE PROMISED HIM THE MOST BEAUTIFUL WOMAN IN THE WORLD AS A BRIBE. WHEN PRIAM SENT PARIS TO SPARTA, APHRODITE DELIVERED HER REWARD: PARIS FELL IN LOVE WITH HELEN, AND SHE WITH HIM, AND HE BROUGHT HER BACK TO TROY.

was to take place. Agamemnon and Odysseus rose as Priam approached, and the ritual began. Wine was mixed in a great bowl and Agamemnon drew his knife and cut some tufts of wool from the lambs' heads. The tufts were passed around to the Greek and Trojan captains. Then Agamemnon stepped forward, raised his arms and prayed loudly in his great voice to Zeus on behalf of them all, setting out the terms of the truce and calling on Zeus, the sun, the rivers, oceans, and Earth itself to witness the sacred vow:

If Menelaus falls by Paris' hand,
Be Helen left to Paris with her wealth;
But, if by Menelaus Paris fall,
Restored be Helen and her wealth by Troy,
And such atonement to our host withal,
As may be bruited in far times to come.
But if Dardanian Priam or his sons
Withhold the atonement on their champion's fall
I swear in endless battle for that price
To keep me, till I gain the goal of war.

Then he slit the throats of the three lambs, and laid their trembling bodies on the ground. One by one, the chiefs filled their wine cups from the great bowl, and poured libations onto the earth. Greek and Trojan alike could be heard muttering prayers to Zeus full of fierce oaths and vengeful threats if the truce were broken.

Priam was in anguish; he announced that he was going to return to the city as he could not bear to watch the fighting between his son and Menelaus; the outcome was already decided by Zeus and the gods, and there was nothing he could do to change it.

The outcome was already decided by Zeus and the gods.

The fight

Paris and Menelaus prowled toward each other, each trying to stare the other man down.

Hector and Odysseus marked off the combat arena. They dropped two pebbles into a helmet to draw lots, to see who would strike the first blow. Hector shook the helmet until one of the pebbles flew out; Paris had the advantage.

As one man, the soldiers on both sides sat down in ranks, next to their horses and armor. Only Paris and Menelaus were left standing. Slowly Paris began to put on his armor; first the chain mail; then the silver-clasped greaves to protect his legs; then a breastplate, the one that belonged to his brother Lycaon, but fit him so well. He slung his long bronze blade over his shoulder, strapped his great shield onto his arm and put on his helmet with its bristling horsehair crest; finally he grasped his thick-staffed spear. And Menelaus followed every step of the way, putting on his own armor. The two warriors stood ready.

The Greeks and Trojans began whooping and yelling. Paris and Menelaus prowled toward each other shaking their spears, each trying to stare the other man down. As agreed by lot, Paris made the first move; he hurled his great spear. It flew straight and true and hit dead center of Menelaus' shield, but it did not break through—the spear tip was bent aside. Then Menelaus shook his spear in the air and screamed to the gods:

> *Grant me that now on Alexander's head*
> *I visit with this vengeance the foul deed*
> *He did me, and o'erthrow him by my arm*
> *That latest generations shrink appall'd*
> *From crime disloyal to a generous host.*

He threw his spear. It slammed into Paris' shield, bursting through the strong hide, on through his breastplate, and the chainmail and even the linen tunic underneath. But Paris swerved, dodging the full force of the weapon, and suffered only a scratch. While

Paris and Menelaus fought one-to-one over Helen. Menelaus was getting the upper hand, but Aphrodite spirited Paris away from the battlefield to the safety of his luxury apartments, much to everyone's disgust, including Helen.

he was recovering, Menelaus drew his sword and brought it crashing down on Paris' helmet, but the sword shattered on the horsehair crest. Beside himself, Menelaus seized him by the crest of his helmet and swung him round. The chinstrap was cutting into Paris' throat, choking him. Menelaus almost had him—but Aphrodite intervened, snapping the strap so that the helmet came off in Menelaus' hand; thwarted, he flung it into the ranks of his men. While they scrambled for the trophy, Menelaus grabbed a second spear and looked round wild-eyed for Paris, but Aphrodite had snatched up her darling boy and whisked him back to the perfumed comfort of his apartments.

Paris and Helen

Having rescued Paris, Aphrodite disguised herself as an old seamstress and bustled off to find Helen, sidling up to her and whispering:

> *Follow; for Paris calls thee to his side.*
> *There in his chamber on the carven couch*
> *Glistening in beauty and attire he lies;*
> *Nor couldst thou deem him from a mortal fray*
> *Hardly return'd, but rather issuing forth*
> *To dance, or resting in the pause of dance.*

Aphrodite was tremendously pleased with herself; she had rescued Paris and there he was, groomed and perfumed—you would never think he had been fighting. But Helen was furious; she saw the goddess in the crone, the arching neck, the shining eyes, the swelling breasts, but was too angry to be afraid of challenging the most fickle deity on Olympus. What was Aphrodite doing here? If Aphrodite was so fond of the coward Paris she could make love to him herself:

> *Nay, go there thou, cleave to his side, for him*
> *Forsake the paths of heaven, and know no more*
> *The pavement of Olympus 'neath thy tread;*
> *But tend and weep upon him, till he deign*
> *To make thee wife—or leman! I go not;*
> *'Twere shame to me again to lie with him,*
> *The mock of Trojan women till I die!*

ΠΑΡΙΣ

ΕΛΕΝΗ

Paris met Helen at Sparta, where he was sent by his father Priam on a diplomatic mission. Although married to Menelaus, Helen fell in love with Paris, and they eloped, taking a large amount of Menelaus' treasury with them.

Aphrodite snapped back in fury, showing her true colors, and warning Helen that she could easily turn both Greeks and Trojans against her, and leave her with no place to hide. And Helen, even though she was a daughter of Zeus, cringed under the onslaught, and followed the goddess in unwilling silence.

They went to Paris' rooms, where Aphrodite made Helen sit down face to face with Paris; yet she would not look at him, and lashed out at him:

> *Return'd from battle! Aye, but would to Heaven*
> *Thou hadst died rather by the strong right arm*
> *Of him my other husband! Oft wouldst boast*
> *Thyself than Menelaus by thy mould*
> *And might and fence the better: forth then, forth,*
> *And give defiance to a second fight!*
> *But I, who know thee, bid thee rather rest*
> *Quiet from war, not reckless dare to meet*
> *Atreus' fair Son in single combat more;*
> *Haply the second time he slays thee quite!*

Paris spoke gently to his wife, weaving the old familiar spell, with Aphrodite's help. He explained that Menelaus may have won the day (with the help of Athena) but that he would fight again tomorrow. Meanwhile Helen was as irresistibly beautiful as the day he first saw her and he couldn't wait to take her to his great carved bed. He led the way, and Helen, weakened by Aphrodite's power, followed him willingly.

While Paris and Helen lost themselves in the soft pillows of lustful love, Menelaus stormed up and down the lines like an enraged lion, looking for Paris. Where had he gone? The Trojans certainly weren't hiding him—they now loathed him almost as much as the Greeks did. Agamemnon seized the time, claimed victory for Menelaus, and invoked the terms of the oath:

> *Hear me, ye Dardans, Troy, and Troy's Allies!*
> *Victory is manifest unto the arm*
> *Of Menelaus; therefore yield ye up*
> *Argeian Helen and her wealth withal,*
> *And likewise such atonement to our host*
> *As shall be bruited in far times to come.*

And behind him, the Greek army roared their approval.

APHRODITE

THE GODDESS OF LOVE, DESIRE, AND SEXUAL PASSION, APHRODITE WAS EITHER A DAUGHTER OF ZEUS AND DIONE, OR BORN SPONTANEOUSLY FROM SEA FOAM ON THE COAST OF CYPRUS. SHE HAD THE POWER TO MAKE EVERY MORTAL—AND ALL THE GODS EXCEPT ATHENA, ARTEMIS, AND HESTIA—FALL HELPLESSLY IN LOVE. IT WAS HER POWER AND GIFTS OF BEAUTY THAT MADE PARIS AND HELEN IRRESISTIBLE TO EACH OTHER, REGARDLESS OF THE COSTS IN OTHER MEN'S LIVES—THE POWER OF LOVE THAT IGNITED THE WAR.

Book 4
THE TRUCE IS BROKEN

Discord on Olympus

INSTANT *ILIAD*

THE GODS ARE
HOLDING A COUNCIL
MEETING ON OLYMPUS.
TO ANNOY HERA,
WHO WANTS TO
DESTROY TROY, ZEUS
PROPOSES THAT—
NOW THE VICTORY
SEEMS TO HAVE GONE
TO THE GREEKS—IT
MIGHT BE TIME TO
MAKE PEACE. BUT
ATHENA AND HERA
MUTTER TO EACH
OTHER, PLOTTING
AGAINST THE
TROJANS AND
SEETHING WITH FURY
AGAINST ZEUS.
ATHENA GOES DOWN
TO THE BATTLEFIELD
AND PROVOKES THE
TROJANS INTO
BREAKING THE TRUCE.

Enraged by Zeus' needling, Hera urged him to take some account of all the effort she had made fomenting war in the first place:

> *Most dread our Lord! What falleth from thy lips?*
> *Hast thou the heart to make of no avail*
> *The toil, wherewith I sweated to and fro,*
> *The labour—yea, my chariot's steeds wax'd faint*
> *With those my wanderings to collect this host,*
> *To work this woe on Priam's sons?*

Zeus replied by asking what the Trojans had ever done to Hera to deserve this punishment. He revealed that Troy was his favorite city. What would Hera do if he decided to turn his full anger on one of her favored towns, Argos, Sparta, or Mycenae? Hera agreed that Zeus had the right to destroy them if they angered him, but insisted that as a goddess she had the same rights. Not wanting to cause a serious division in Olympus, she suggested that they agree to let each other have their own way, after which the other gods would follow their example. So Zeus commanded Athena to go down to the battle lines, if she wanted to, to try to get the Trojans to be the first to break their oaths of truce.

Athena was anyway impatient for action, and she shot down from Olympus like a blazing meteor, emitting sparks to earth, and leaped into the mass of troops. The Greeks and Trojans were awe-struck at the sight, and looked at each other with fear, afraid that this was a sign that war would begin again. While the two sides were talking to each other, Athena disguised herself as the Trojan spearman Laodocus, and

The Olympian gods: clockwise from the top: Zeus, Artemis, Hephaestus, Hestia, Ares, Aphrodite, Hermes, Demeter, Apollo, Hera, Poseidon, and Athena. Not all the gods lived on Olympus all the time, and not all of them featured in the Iliad.

Agamemnon

was horrified

and swore to

Menelaus that

the Trojans

would pay for

breaking the

truce.

sought out the mighty and handsome Pandarus, standing next to the powerful force of shield-bearers that had come from the Aesepus River under his command. She incited him immediately to break the truce:

> Wilt thou obey me and collect thy heart
> To aim an arrow swift at Atreus' Son?
> No Trojan, but would give thee thanks and praise;
> And of all Trojans Paris most, the prince:
> Costly the guerdon first of all the host
> From him wouldst thou receive, if e'er he saw
> The dreaded son of Atreus, Menelas,
> Quell'd by thy dart, and stretch'd upon his pyre.

Pandarus was persuaded by this, and took his polished bow, which was over three feet across, made from the horns of a fully grown wild goat he had shot himself. As his troops surrounded him with their shields for protection, he bent the bow firmly against the ground to string it. Then he lifted the lid of his quiver and took out a brand-new feathered arrow, filled with the power of pain. As he put the arrow against the string, he promised Apollo the archer-god an enormous offering of firstborn lambs once he had returned home. He pulled back the string until it was touching his chest and the iron tip rested next to the bow, then loosed the arrow toward the enemy ranks.

But Zeus' daughter Athena did not forget Menelaus, and stood in front of him to deflect the arrow, guiding it carefully to where his body armor overlapped his belt. The arrow hit the belt, drove through the armor, and grazed his skin just enough to draw blood, which ran down his thighs to his ankles. Agamemnon was horrified at this sight, and swore to Menelaus that the Trojans would pay for breaking the truce with the destruction of their city. But he was worried that when the Greeks discovered that Menelaus had been killed they would flee the battle and return home.

Menelaus hastened to reassure him, explaining that the arrow had not given him a dangerous wound. Nonetheless Agamemnon sent for the healer Machaon. When Machaon reached the spot, the Greek commanders gathered in a circle round Menelaus, and watched Machaon extract the arrow, suck out the blood, and apply healing herbs which had been given to his father by the centaur Cheiron.

While this was happening, the Trojans were advancing to attack again. The Greeks began to put their armor back on, once more willing to continue the fight. Agamemnon set aside his customary bronze chariot and made his way around the Greek army on foot, encouraging them:

Heroes of Argos! Let not now relax
Your wonted mettle: not to falsehood's side
Will Father Zeus incline him. Soon, I ween,
Shall they, who first forsworn transgress'd the truce,
Be torn by ravening vultures limb from limb,
Leaving to us to bear across the seas
Their wives and children from their homes despoil'd!

When he came across some troops who were reluctant to fight, he shouted at them:

Feel ye no shame? O ye to evil doom'd,
Argeians, foul reproaches to the name!
Why droop ye, numb and broken, ev'n as fawns
That with a flight exhausted o'er the plain
Droop at the last, all strength within them gone;
So droop ye, numb and broken, loth to war.
Or would ye tarry till Troy makes her way
Far as your galleys' moorings on the shore,
Tempting great Zeus—if he will save ye there?

Agamemnon came to the Cretans, led by Idomeneus, and urged him on, telling him there was nobody on the battlefield he honored more. Idomeneus shouted back enthusiastically: now that the Trojans had broken the oaths of truth, they could expect nothing but death and disaster. Next Agamemnon found the two brothers, Ajax and Teucer, with a swarm of foot soldiers behind them, putting on their helmets. Agamemnon knew that these brave warriors needed no encouragement from him. He found the elderly Nestor, who had put his chariots and horses in the front, and his bravest infantry as a rearguard, so that the less willing in the middle would be forced to fight. Then Agamemnon ran into two detachments that were standing idle, the horse-driver Menestheus and his Athenian troops, and Odysseus with his Cephallenian troops. Neither had yet heard the call to battle and Agamemnon rebuked them, accusing them of waiting for the other Greeks to do the fighting.

Odysseus retorted that Agamemnon was full of pompous rage, and Agamemnon grinned and apologized. But when he then found Diomedes waiting with his horses and chariots, he angrily accused him also of being better at talking than at fighting, and a disgrace to his father Tydeus. Diomedes did not reply, but Capaneus

ATHENA

ATHENA WAS THE GODDESS OF WISDOM —A JOB THAT SHE COMBINED WITH BEING GODDESS OF WAR—AND THE DAUGHTER OF ZEUS AND METIS. HOMER REFERRED TO HER AS "LADY OF THE GLEAMING EYES," AND SHE HAD DUAL RESPONSIBILITIES IN THE *ILIAD*. ALTHOUGH SHE WAS GODDESS OF THE CITY OF TROY, SHE WAS ACTUALLY ON THE GREEKS' SIDE, AND HAD A PARTICULAR FONDNESS—BECAUSE OF HIS WISDOM—FOR ODYSSEUS.

MENELAUS

standing next to him argued back. He asserted their superiority to both their fathers, who had been destroyed through their own recklessness. But Diomedes would have none of it:

> *Rest thee in silence, friend, and wait my word.*
> *To Agamemnon, shepherd of the host,*
> *I give no blame, that, as he may, he speaks*
> *To rouse to war Achaia's mailèd men.*
> *To him will be the glory, should we take*
> *Proud Ilion, and destroy the host of Troy;*
> *And his the heaviest sorrow, should we fail.*
> *Haste rather; put we on our olden might.*

As he spoke, Diomedes leaped fully armed from his chariot and charged into action, the bronze armor ringing on his chest. Meanwhile, the Greeks marched silently into battle, wave on wave, the only sound the orders from the commanders. There was a hubbub from the Trojan forces, all speaking at once with their different dialects and languages, and the gods swept down to fill the opposing armies with loathing for each other.

The two front lines met, with a clash of shields and spears. The air rang with the screams of the dying and the jeers of the victors, and the earth began to run with blood. The roar of the battle sounded like wild mountain torrents surging through deep ravines to crash together and plunge thunderously into a mighty gorge. Antilochus killed Echepolus, piercing his helmet and forehead with a spear. The leader of the Abantes, Elephenor, grabbed him by the feet as he fell and tried to drag the body away to strip the armor, but he in turn was struck down by the Trojan Agenor. The Greeks and Trojans fell upon each other like wolves.

Ajax's spear passed through the chest of the young Trojan Simoisius, who fell dead to the ground. In response, Priam's son Antiphus hurled a spear toward Ajax. It missed him, but instead hit one of Odysseus' comrades, Leucus, in the groin, just as he was dragging Simoisius' body away. Odysseus was enraged by this, and his bronze armor glittered as he moved up to the front line. Carefully choosing his target, he threw his spear. The Trojans leaped out of the way, but the spear hit one of Priam's illegitimate sons, Democoön, in the temple. The blow was so powerful that the spear went right through his head and out of the other side. He fell dead, his armor clattering about him.

This was such a shocking sight that Hector and the Trojan front line fell back, and the Greeks gave a great shout and pushed forward. The god Apollo was watching this from Pergamus, the highest point in Troy, and urged on the Trojans with indignation:

> *Rouse ye, O chieftains-charioteers of Troy!*
> *Yield not to Argos in the fight this day:*
> *Not stone their flesh, nor iron, proof to blows,*
> *Let spear or sword but strike them! Know, withal,*
> *No longer doth the fairhair'd Thetis' son,*
> *The dread Achilles, range in fight, but now*
> *Broods in his galleys, sullen, and withdrawn.*

At the same time, the Greeks were being encouraged by Zeus' daughter, Athena, who made her way through the ranks, urging forward any soldiers she saw holding back. The Greek Diores was hit by a jagged stone on the right ankle, and he fell in the dust, the bones and tendons severed. The man who had thrown it, Thracian leader Peirous, ran forward and stabbed him in the belly with his spear. His intestines gushed out and darkness engulfed him. As Peirous sprang away, the Greek warrior Thoas struck him in the chest with a spear and then finished him off with his sword. But before Thoas could get hold of Peirous' valuable armor, the Thracians had surrounded his body, and forced a retreat. Soon Trojans and Greeks were lying dead in their multitudes, stretched out next to each other, face down in the dust.

Soon Trojans and Greeks were lying dead in their multitudes.

Even though the legendary Achilles was not fighting, the rest of the Greek heroes, and those from Troy, fought long and hard.

Book 5
THE HEROICS OF DIOMEDES

Athena and Diomedes

The goddess Athena inspired Diomedes with great courage and resolve to go into the heart of the battle. She kindled divine fire from his shield and helmet:

> ... From off his helm
> And buckler she made burn a quenchless fire:
> Bright as the brightest of the stars of heaven
> Fresh from the Ocean comes the Autumn-star;
> Such from his shoulders and his crest the fire
> She kindled; and she urged him through the fray
> Into the midst, where thickest throng'd the war.

Athena rode with Diomedes in his chariot; with her help, strength, and encouragement he mowed down several Trojans and wounded both Aphrodite and Ares, two of the gods who supported the Trojan side.

Two wealthy Trojan brothers, Phegeus and Idaeus, saw Diomedes coming and threw themselves against him in their chariot. Filled with Athena's bravery, Diomedes went toward them on foot. Phegeus threw a spear but it flew past Diomedes' left shoulder. Diomedes hit back with his own spear, striking Phegeus in the chest and knocking him out of the chariot. Idaeus leaped out as well and fled, but was rescued by the god Hephaestus, who smothered him in night, so that his father might not be completely broken by grief through losing both his sons. Diomedes grabbed their horses and told his soldiers to take them back to the Greek ships.

Pleased with what she had achieved, Athena took the war god Ares aside and persuaded him to leave the battle, and allow Zeus to decide whether the Trojans or the Greeks would win:

> *Ares, O Ares, pest to mortal kind,*
> *Their cities' terror, and their bloody scourge!*
> *Were it not our better part to leave these hosts*
> *(Whether to Argos or to Troy Zeus grant*
> *The victory) still to battle, but ourselves*
> *Departing so avoid our Father's wrath?*

With Ares out of the way, the Greeks were able to push the Trojans back and each of the Greek leaders overcame his Trojan opponent. Diomedes stormed into the Trojan ranks like a tidal wave, spreading death and confusion as he went. He was watched by the Trojan Pandarus, who took aim with his bow and hit Diomedes in the right shoulder. Pandarus shouted with delight, urging on the Trojans and boasting that the arrow must

Diomedes stormed into the Trojan ranks like a tidal wave.

have been fatal because Zeus himself was speeding him on. But he was wrong. The arrow had gone through Diomedes' armor and drawn blood, but instead of collapsing, he urged his charioteer to come and pull the arrow out. With a gush of blood, the arrow came out of his shoulder, and Diomedes prayed to Athena to let him kill Pandarus:

> *Grant me to come within the reach of spear*
> *And slay the man who hath forestall'd me now*
> *And vaunts so loudly, it shall ne'er be mine*
> *To see the sunshine of another day!*

Athena heard his prayer and revitalized Diomedes' limbs, removing the mist from his eyes so that he could tell the difference on the battlefield between the men and the gods. She warned him not to fight with any of the gods, with one exception—Zeus' daughter Aphrodite.

Diomedes attacks Aphrodite

Diomedes had been determined to get back into the battle even before the relief that Athena had brought him. Now he had three times the determination of an ordinary man, and had been roused to even greater fury than before. He charged back into the Trojan line, killing as he went, and stripping his victims of their armor.

This slaughter was witnessed by the Trojan prince Aeneas, who sought out Pandarus and asked what had happened to his reputation as an archer. He pointed out the rampaging Diomedes in the distance, saying that he was causing havoc in the Trojan ranks. Pandarus replied that he had already shot Diomedes once, and that some god must be protecting him:

> *... By his side*
> *Stands some Immortal in a cloud conceal'd,*
> *And turn'd my dart at point to pierce him through.*
> *Already have I shot, and struck him full*
> *On the right shoulder through the hauberk's edge,*
> *And vaunted I should send him ere his time*
> *To Hades, yet subdued him not at all:*
> *Some God, be sure, is anger'd with us now.*

DIOMEDES

THE KING OF ARGOS, THE SON OF TYDEUS, AND SECOND ONLY TO ACHILLES ON THE GREEK SIDE FOR HIS BRAVERY AND FEATS OF ARMS. HE BROUGHT AS MANY AS 80 SHIPS TO TROY AND INSPIRED CONSIDERABLE ASSISTANCE FROM THE GODDESS ATHENA WHEN HE FOUND HIMSELF ON THE BATTLEFIELD UP AGAINST HECTOR AND AENEAS—EVEN MANAGING TO WOUND THE GODDESS APHRODITE AND THE WAR GOD ARES.

Pandarus complained bitterly that he had shot Menelaus and Diomedes, and drawn blood, but it had only driven them on. He swore to hurl his bow into the fire if he ever got back home.

Aeneas urged Pandarus to join him in a chariot to confront Diomedes more closely. They sped off into the battle with Aeneas at the reins. Diomedes' charioteer warned him of their approach, and suggested that Diomedes should avoid the confrontation. But Diomedes refused to hide. He already had his eye on the horses that were drawing the chariot of Aeneas, aware that they were among the best in the world—descended from those that Zeus himself had once given to a Trojan king. They were a worthy prize in the coming encounter.

Pandarus was the first to strike. His spear pierced Diomedes' shield and struck against his breastplate. Pandarus shouted with triumph, but once again he was crowing prematurely. Diomedes threw his spear and Athena directed it straight into Pandarus' face and through his head. It was a fatal blow, and his horses shied away.

Aeneas leaped down to protect the corpse, and stood over it shouting. With superhuman strength, Diomedes picked up a gigantic boulder and flung it at Aeneas, crushing his thigh bone. Aeneas sank to his knees in pain, and would certainly have been killed had not his mother, the goddess Aphrodite, flung her cloak around her son to protect him from the flying spears and carried him away from the battle.

Diomedes remembered his instructions from Athena and made off in pursuit of Aphrodite. When he caught up with her, he lunged at her with his spear and pierced the palm of her hand, and her immortal blood ran out onto the ground. Aphrodite screamed and dropped her son, but Apollo wrapped him up in a blue cloud for safety. In great pain, the goddess swept from the battlefield, found the resting war god Ares, and begged him to lend her his chariot to take her home to Olympus. When Aphrodite arrived at the dwelling of the gods she was comforted by her mother, Dione, but Athena mocked her for her love of the Trojans, and asked if she had scratched her dainty hand. Zeus advised Aphrodite to leave off warfare and keep to her own realm, the marriage bed.

The gods return to the fray

Although he knew that Apollo was now protecting Aeneas, Diomedes still threw himself at him, but Apollo repelled each attack. At his fourth charge, Apollo warned Diomedes off:

AENEAS

THE TROJAN HERO AENEAS, LEADER OF THE DARDANIANS, WAS THE SEMIDIVINE SON OF ANCHISES AND APHRODITE, WHICH IS WHY THE GODS WERE SO EAGER TO INTERVENE TO SAVE HIM. TWICE THEY DID SO DURING THE *ILIAD* —APHRODITE SAVING HIM FROM DIOMEDES, AND POSEIDON FROM ACHILLES. HE WAS ONE OF THE FEW TROJAN LEADERS TO ESCAPE THE SLAUGHTER AT THE FALL OF TROY, AND LEGEND HAS IT THAT HIS DESCENDANTS WENT ON TO BE FOUNDERS OF ROME AND KINGS OF ANCIENT BRITAIN.

Warn thee, Tydides, and withdraw thee hence:
Match not thyself in thought the peer to Gods.
Liken not unto men who walk the earth
The immortal generation of the Gods.

Apollo spirited Aeneas away to his temple in Troy to be healed, and replaced him with a ghost, so that the Trojans and Greeks battled it out around what they thought was Aeneas' fallen form. Apollo urged Ares to return to the battle to drive Diomedes away, so Ares disguised himself and began to rally the Trojans, urging them to protect Aeneas. His cry was taken up by Hector, and soon the Trojan army was turning to fight, helped by a veil of darkness that Ares had thrown over the battlefield. Apollo fetched the renewed Aeneas back, and his appearance roused the Trojan troops further.

The Greek leaders stood firm, rallied by Agamemnon. Even so, Aeneas killed two of their best fighters, the twins Crethon and Orsilochus, drawing Menelaus into the heart of the battle to take revenge. The god Ares, disguised as a Thracian, saw him and determined that he should be vanquished at the hands of Aeneas. But Antilochus set off in pursuit to protect Menelaus and the two stood side by side. Aeneas withdrew when he saw the two Greeks standing together and they managed to retrieve the dead bodies of Crethon and Orsilochus.

Hector had been watching from across the other side of the battle, and now he rushed shouting toward Menelaus and Antilochus, supported by the war god Ares. At long last this sight unnerved Diomedes, who realized that Hector had Ares by his side, and he urged those around him to retreat. He remembered Athena's advice not to be drawn into battle with gods.

Slowly the Greeks became aware that Ares was at work on the Trojan side, and fell back before the onslaught of Hector and his comrades. Above them in Olympus, Hera and Athena had also realized that Ares was once more on the battlefield, and they resolved to intervene in the defense of the Greeks. Hera prepared her chariot with its bronze wheels and gold-bedecked horses. Athena put on Zeus' own armor and her golden helmet, and slung the aegis of Zeus across her shoulders. Hera asked for Zeus' permission to teach the madman Ares a lesson in war, and Zeus sent them on their way with his blessing. Together Athena and Hera whipped the horses and thundered out of the gates of Olympus.

Leaving their horses hidden in a mist near Troy, the goddesses made the final part of the journey on foot. They arrived where the Greeks were gathered around Diomedes and Hera urged them on:

> *Shame on you! Noble to the eye alone!*
> *Argeians, foul reproaches to the name!*
> *Of yore, when great Achilles came to war,*
> *Never beyond the Dardan gates durst Troy*
> *Adventure; such the terror of his spear;*
> *Now from the city to your fleet they range.*

The Greeks swelled with renewed courage, while Athena made straight for Diomedes who was wiping the blood from the wound made by Pandarus' spear. The goddess teased Diomedes for his timidity. He recognized her and replied that he was simply abiding by her instructions not to fight any gods except for Aphrodite. Now the god Ares was carrying everything before him on the battlefield. But Athena took her place beside Diomedes as his charioteer, and told him not to fear Ares now that she was with him. She commanded Diomedes to attack Ares directly.

Their chariot stormed forward, groaning with their weight, and Athena covered herself with a cap of invisibility. Ares was busy stripping his victims of their precious armor. When he saw Diomedes coming, he abandoned his looting and made straight for him. He lunged at him with a spear, but Athena caught it and pushed it away above their chariot. Then Athena guided Diomedes' spear so that it drove straight through Ares' protective clothing and into his belly. Ares let out a terrifying roar, which stopped the frightened soldiers on both sides for a moment, and he rose in a cloud to Olympus, straight to the side of Zeus.

Ares accused Zeus of encouraging Athena in her lawless behavior and urged him to bring his daughter under control. But Zeus was contemptuous:

> *Make not thy moan, false Traitor! at my side.*
> *Most of Olympians loathe I thee, whose care*
> *Is all of blood and battle, strife and death.*
> *On thee thy mother's mood accursed hath fallen,*
> *Still stubborn, insupportable, untamed,*
> *Whom scarce by hardest words can I subdue.*

Despite his loathing for his pestilential son, Zeus called for Ares to be healed, because he would not allow a child of his to suffer pain for long. Ares sat down at Zeus' side, his murderous involvement in the battle checked, and Hera and Athena, their work done, returned to the halls of the gods.

ARES

THE BLOODTHIRSTY AND WHOLLY UNRELIABLE GOD OF WAR, THE SON OF ZEUS AND HERA. HOMER DESCRIBED HIM AS BEING A "BUTCHER OF MEN" AND THE "BREAKER OF SHIELDS," BUT HE WAS NOT ABSOLUTELY INVINCIBLE—BETWEEN THEM, ATHENA AND DIOMEDES MANAGED TO DRIVE HIM FROM THE BATTLEFIELD OUTSIDE THE WALLS OF TROY. IT WAS RUMORED THAT HE WAS IN LOVE WITH APHRODITE.

Book 6
HECTOR AND ANDROMACHE

The Greeks in the ascendant

INSTANT *ILIAD*

THE BATTLE
CONTINUES WITHOUT
INTERFERENCE FROM
THE GODS, AND THE
TROJANS ARE BEING
DRIVEN BACK. HECTOR
GOES BACK INTO THE
CITY TO ROUSE HIS
BROTHER PARIS TO
PLAY HIS PART IN THE
BATTLE, AND HE URGES
THE WOMEN OF TROY
TO PRAY TO THE
GODS FOR HELP.

The struggle between the two armies continued to rage with neither side gaining the advantage. Then Great Ajax managed to break the Trojan line by felling one of the tallest Trojans, Acamas, with his bronze spear:

> *... But him he smote*
> *Full on the vizor of the horse-plumed helm;*
> *Piercing the brow and crashing through the skull*
> *Pass'd the brass-point; and darkness veil'd his eyes.*

Ajax's success led to a murderous assault by Odysseus and Agamemnon and some of the leading Greeks, including Euryalus, who killed no less than four warriors. Then the Trojan Adrestus lost control of his chariot and his horses became caught up in a tamarisk bush, snapping the shaft and throwing him out face down in the dust. When he became aware of his surroundings, he realized that Menelaus was standing over him, armed with a spear. Adrestus flung his arms around Menelaus' knees and begged his mercy. Pleading, he offered Menelaus an enormous ransom from his father if only Menelaus would spare his life.

Menelaus was about to agree when Agamemnon ran over, shouting at him not to be so tender-hearted:

> *Sparest thou the Trojans? Menelaus, thou*
> *My brother! Suits it thee to show this ruth?*
> *They dealt by thee forsooth so graciously,*
> *Thou needs must thus reward them! Nay, let none*

Escape the bloody ruin that we bring;
Fighting or fleeing, perish all alike;
Mothers, and infants in the womb unborn!
Perish from off the earth the accursed race,
Uncoffin'd, swallow'd up in endless night!

On hearing this, Menelaus changed his mind and pushed Adrestus away from him, and Agamemnon stabbed him through the side. At the same time, Nestor was urging the Greeks to slay the Trojans without pausing to gather plunder and armor. Driven on by Nestor's words, the Greeks pushed the Trojans back toward the city walls.

On the Trojan side, the prophet Helenus—one of Priam's sons—was in conference with Aeneas and Hector, aware that the Trojan lines were about to collapse. He implored the two leaders to rally the Trojans to hold the city gates, lest they all fled back to their wives. Helenus also told Hector to ask his mother Hecabe to gather the older women of Troy at the temple of Athena to make a sacrifice. He said that if Hector's mother offered the most beautiful robe from her palace to Athena, together with a dozen year-old heifers, then Athena might have pity on the town and hold back the fearsome Diomedes:

For not Achilles' self, whom goddess-born
They boast, and prince of men, e'er fill'd our souls
With panic like This Man, whose spirit flames
Infuriate, nor in battle finds he peer.

Hector moved among the Trojan troops right across the battlefield, brandishing two spears, and inspired them to rally so effectively that some of their enemies wondered what divine help they were receiving. At last the Greeks began to give ground. Having achieved some respite, Hector set off into the city.

Diomedes and Glaucus

As Hector left, two warriors came into the space between the armies to face each other. From the Greek side came Diomedes, who challenged the other to identify himself. Diomedes praised the Trojan's courage but insisted that he say whether he was mortal or divine:

HECTOR

COMMANDER-IN-CHIEF OF ALL OF THE TROJAN ARMIES, HECTOR WAS THE ELDEST SON OF PRIAM AND HECABE, AND MARRIED TO ANDROMACHE, THE DAUGHTER OF THE KING OF THEBES. WHILE ACHILLES WAS MOTIVATED BY PASSION, VANITY, AND RAGE, HIS GREAT ADVERSARY HECTOR WAS MOTIVATED PRIMARILY BY DUTY.

BELLEROPHON

GLAUCUS WAS A
GOLDEN-ARMORED
PRINCE FROM LYCIA,
ONE OF PRIAM'S ALLIES.
HIS GRANDFATHER
WAS THE LEGENDARY
BELLEROPHON, WHO
WAS TO BE PUT TO
DEATH BECAUSE OF
THE LIES OF A QUEEN
WHOSE ADVANCES HE
REJECTED, AND WAS
FORCED TO CARRY
OUT THREE IMPOSSIBLE
MISSIONS BY THE
LYCIAN KING. WHEN
BELLEROPHON
SUCCEEDED, THE KING
MARRIED HIM TO HIS
OWN DAUGHTER AND
MADE HIM HIS HEIR.
THE MERE MENTION OF
BELLEROPHON WAS
ENOUGH TO MAKE
GLAUCUS AND
DIOMEDES BREAK OFF
FROM FIGHTING AND
EXCHANGE THEIR
ARMOR.

Who art thou, noble warrior? God or man?
For never till this moment saw I thee,
Where men seek glory in the van of war:
Yet now my heart hath lifted thee beyond
All others, who hast dared to bide my spear.
Hapless the fathers, whose dear sons meet me!
But, if thou hast descended down from heaven,
Against the Powers of heaven I will not war.

In reply, the Trojan, Glaucus, told Diomedes the tale of his grandfather, the handsome Bellerophon. He had had the misfortune of inspiring the obsessive love of the wife of his lord, who lied about him, telling her husband that Bellerophon had tried to seduce her. As a punishment, Bellerophon was sent to Lycia with a fatal message that would guarantee his death. The ruler of Lycia read the message, and sent him to kill the frightful monster called the Chimaera, then the fearsome tribe of warriors known as the Solymi, then the Amazon women. When he succeeded, the ruler recognized Bellerophon's qualities, married him to his daughter and gave him half his kingdom.

Diomedes was delighted by this story, and stuck his spear harmlessly in the ground, to show that he would not attack. He revealed that his grandfather had once entertained Bellerophon, and they had exchanged splendid gifts. Diomedes declared that he and Glaucus should not fight:

... Be thou my friend
Therefore in Lycia when perchance I come,
And I am thine in Argos. Likewise here
Let each the other shun amid the throng.
Many of these far nations and of Troy;
Cast on my sword by heaven, or in their flight
O'ertaken, I can slay without a pang;
So too slay thou of Argos whom thou mayst.
Rather let us make interchange of gift,
Thy arms for mine; so all the host shall know
Us friends, even as our fathers were before us.

Both leaped down from their chariots and took each other by the hand and exchanged their armor. In this, Glaucus made an extremely bad deal, because he exchanged his golden armor for Diomedes' bronze, worth ten times less than his own.

Hector at home with his wife Andromache. Hector's home life, and his love of his wife and son, give him something to live for other than war, which is all that Achilles, the killing machine, has to look forward to in his own short life.

The Trojan women

When Hector reached the oak tree at the city gates, he was besieged by wives and daughters clamoring to know about their husbands, fathers, and friends. Knowing that many of them faced grief as soon as the full news of the battle reached them, Hector told them to pray to the gods. He moved on toward Priam's magnificent palace and the fifty rooms of polished stone where Priam's sons slept with their wives. There was his mother, Hecabe, who took his hand and offered him some wine. Hector refused, but told her instead to gather the older women of the town and go to Athena's temple to beg her to keep Diomedes away from Troy. Meanwhile Hector went on to find Paris and rouse him to play some part in the defense of the city. Hecabe did as she was asked, urging the women to get ready to follow her to the temple, and then going down to the scented closet where she kept her embroidered robes, woven by women from Sidon brought to Troy by Paris. She picked out the longest and most beautiful as a gift for Athena. When the door to the temple was opened, the women joined the priestess in a loud wail, lifting their hands to heaven and praying to the goddess to restrain Diomedes: but despite their lamentations, Athena just turned her face away.

Hector made his way to the lovely house where Paris lived, in the heights of the town near the homes of Priam and Hector himself. He found Paris in his bedroom, polishing his beautiful armor and checking his bow, while Helen and her waiting maids sat with him. The sight annoyed Hector:

> *Up, up, my brother! shame on this thy mood!*
> *Lo round the city all beneath the walls*
> *The people perish, battling for thy sake.*
> *For thee, for thee are all these ringing cries.*

Far from being angered, Paris accepted his brother's criticism. But he promised that he was not sulking and held no grudge against the Trojans. Paris admitted that he had intended to wallow in grief, but his wife had urged him to get back to the fighting, and he had agreed. He asked Hector to give him time to arm himself for the battle, and then he would follow.

Hector did not reply. But Helen then asked her brother-in-law to sit down. She acknowledged that nobody in Troy bore a greater burden of responsibility than did Hector, and that it was all because of her, and Paris' madness in carrying her off. She declared that Zeus clearly had something terrible in store for them—something that people who have yet to be born would sing about in the future. Helen bewailed the fact that she had so weak a husband, who showed no concern for the contempt his colleagues felt for him. She admitted that she was afraid that Paris would pay for this one day. Hector thanked her but refused to sit down, urging her only to get Paris ready for battle and send him out to catch up with him before he had left the city. Hector then left, saying that he was going to see his wife and son in case he was killed in the forthcoming battle.

When Hector reached his house nearby, there was no sign of his wife Andromache or his little boy. He asked the servant if she was visiting one of his sisters or sisters-in-law, or whether she had gone to Athena's temple. The servant said that Andromache had gone onto the city walls in tears to watch the battle. So Hector dashed out of the house, retracing his steps through the streets of Troy. He had just reached the gate when Andromache rushed down from the walls to meet him. Behind her ran the maid with their baby son. Hector smiled at the sight of his son, and Andromache broke down and wept, begging him not to return to the battlefield:

> Hector! This daring needs must be thy death;
> Nor tak'st thou thought of this thine infant son,
> Nor me, thy wife ill-fated, soon to be
> Thy widow; for the foe shall soon assail
> And slay thee at some vantage. Oh for me,
> Better, forlorn of thee, to die forthwith!

Andromache reminded him that her father and her seven brothers had all been killed by Achilles, and her mother had died after her release by

Achilles, too. She declared passionately that Hector was now her father, her mother, her brother, and her husband all rolled into one, and she entreated him to stay on the tower and not go into the battle.

Hector replied that he had to go, or else he would be shamed before the whole city:

> *Yea, wife; thy cares are also mine. But shame—*
> *Women and men alike would cry me shame,*
> *If I recoil'd a craven from the war.*
> *Nor doth my heart so prompt me. Rather have I*
> *Train'd myself ever to be foremost, brave*
> *Amongst the bravest, so to keep unstain'd*
> *My father's glorious name, and win mine own.*

He declared that his greatest grief was at what would happen to Andromache when she was dragged off by the Greeks. He imagined her in Greece, working away at the loom or carrying water for his enemies, whether she liked it or not. Hector exclaimed that he hoped he would be dead before she was taken away, so that he would not have to suffer the sight.

With that, Hector reached for his son, Astyanax, who shrank back in terror at his father's bronze helmet and horsehair plume. So he took his helmet off, kissed his son and prayed to Zeus that one day Astyanax would delight his mother as ruler of Troy. Giving the boy back to his mother, Hector implored her not to grieve:

> *Dear Heart!, lament not for me overmuch.*
> *My span of life hath been allotted me;*
> *Of this be sure, no man can cut it short.*
> *But never breathed the mortal, or be he brave or base,*
> *Who 'scaped the death ordain'd him from his birth.*

Looking back repeatedly, Andromache walked home and found the servants mourning for Hector even though he was still alive.

By now Paris had put on his armor and was hurrying out of the city, laughing as he ran. Soon he had caught up with Hector and greeted him with apologies for his lateness. Hector remarked on what a strange man Paris was: nobody could accuse him of weakness in battle, and yet he was always on the verge of giving up and refusing to fight. Nonetheless Hector spoke encouraging words to his brother. If Zeus let them drive the Greeks from the land, he said, they would celebrate by drinking to the everlasting gods.

ANDROMACHE AND ASTYANAX

ANDROMACHE WAS HECTOR'S WIFE AND THE DAUGHTER OF THE KING OF THEBES. SHE HAD GOOD REASON TO FEAR ACHILLES. AT THE SACK OF THEBES, ACHILLES HAD KILLED HER FATHER AND SEVEN BROTHERS, SO SHE FEARED THE WORST FOR HER HUSBAND AND HER LITTLE SON ASTYANAX. SHE WAS RIGHT TO BE WORRIED: IF TROY FELL, ASTYANAX WAS DOOMED TO BE FLUNG OVER THE CITY WALLS AND SHE WOULD BE TAKEN TO GREECE AS A PRIZE—GIVEN FIRST TO NEOPTOLEMUS, THE SON OF ACHILLES, THEN MARRIED TO HELENUS, HECTOR'S BROTHER.

Book 7
AJAX TAKES ON HECTOR

Hector's challenge

Paris and Hector burst out of the city gate and into the thick of the battle. Together they made great inroads into the Greek army, so that Athena up in Olympus began to become alarmed at the Greek losses. She flew down to the city and met there under an oak tree with Apollo, a supporter of the Trojans, who had followed her down from the dwelling of the gods. They determined to intervene again in the fighting. Apollo urged Athena to take his advice:

> Yet take this better counsel from my lips;
> Consent we yet for one day more to stay
> This battle and this bloodshed; though henceforth
> (Since to you Goddesses it seems so dear
> To wipe fair Ilion clean from the earth)
> They cease not, till the end of Troy be found.

Athena agreed that it was time to stop the fighting for the time being, but wondered how this could be achieved. Apollo suggested that they should rouse Hector to challenge the Greeks to single combat to the death. The Greeks would be honor-bound to agree and the armies would withdraw to witness the duel. As soon as Apollo had spoken, Priam's son, the seer Helenus, sensed what had been decided and went straight to Hector to make the suggestion to him. Helenus assured Hector that the time for his death had not yet come, so he would be safe.

Hector was delighted with the idea. He went out between the opposing armies with his spear and pushed the Trojan front rank back. As they sat down on the ground, Agamemnon managed to persuade the Greeks to do the same. Above them, Apollo and Athena sat like vultures, looking down on line upon line of warriors, with their shields, helmets, and spears glinting like the waves on the sea.

Hector rose to address both armies and offered his challenge. He told the Greeks to send out their champion to fight him alone. Hector offered his terms: if he was killed, his opponent could take his arms and armor, as long as his body was left to be cremated by his own people. If Hector won, he claimed the right to strip off the Greek champion's armor and take it back to Troy and hang it in the temple to Apollo. But he promised to send the body for proper burial:

> ... And men shall sail
> Hereafter those wine-color'd waves, and say:
> 'Yonder an Argive hero lies, of old
> Their bravest, and by glorious Hector slain.'
> So be it; and my fame shall never die.

There was silence when Hector stopped speaking. The Greeks were ashamed to refuse his challenge but afraid to accept it. After a little while, Menelaus reproached them bitterly. He called them a bunch of women and furiously expressed the depths of his humiliation that not one Greek would accept the challenge. Then he announced that he would fight Hector himself and leave the outcome to the gods, and the rest of the Greeks could sit and rot.

Menelaus began to put on his armor, and it would have been for the last time, because Hector was far stronger than he was. But the Greek leaders leaped up and held him back. Agamemnon advised Menelaus not to fight a stronger man just for the sake of a contest, and reminded him that even Achilles was afraid to meet Hector in battle. He said that the Greeks would find someone else to take on Hector. With joy, Menelaus' servants began to remove his armor. Then the elderly Nestor added his reproaches, telling the tale of his valor in combat when he was younger, and declaring that if he were still a young man, Hector would have had a challenger.

Shamed by the condemnation of the old man, nine of the Greeks stood up. Agamemnon was the first, followed quickly by Diomedes, Great Ajax, Odysseus, Little Ajax, the Cretans Idomeneus and Meriones, Eurypylus the king of Cos, and Thoas. They marked their lots and placed them into Agamemnon's helmet, and the troops around them raised their arms to the heavens and prayed that it might be the strongest of them—Ajax, Diomedes, or Agamemnon—who won the draw.

The helmet was shaken and one of the lots leaped out. A herald took it around all nine champions, and it was claimed by Great Ajax:

The Greeks were ashamed to refuse his challenge but afraid to accept it.

> *Friends, friends! The lot is mine, and blithe am I,*
> *Who think to vanquish Hector in these lists.*
> *But while I clothe me in my mail of war,*
> *Offer ye up your prayers to Kronos' Son,*
> *Silently, in your hearts, lest Troy should hear—*
> *Or loudly all—what fear have we of men?*
> *There breathes no man, who, through his greater strength,*
> *Or my own lack of skill, can beat me back.*
> *I was not born, I trow, nor rear'd in arms*
> *At Salamis, to show unpractis'd here!*

The Greeks then prayed to Zeus to oversee the duel, either to answer Ajax's prayer and let him win or else, if Hector was beloved of Zeus as well, to let neither man be beaten and declare a draw.

Dazzling in his bronze armor, Ajax set out with his spear and his shield made of bronze strengthened by seven layers of oxhide, smiling as he went. He looked such a magnificent sight that the knees of the Trojans trembled. Even Hector's heart began to beat faster, but it was too late to change his mind. When Ajax reached the point where Hector stood, he told him that he would now discover what kind of champions the Greeks possessed, even without Achilles. Hector replied that there was no point in trying to scare him like a child:

> *... Well I know*
> *The arts of battle, how to slay my man;*
> *Or to the right or to the left to shift*
> *My dry-tann'd buckler, so to last in fight;*
> *In close encounter to advance a foot*
> *Attuned to Ares' honor, or to guide*
> *My steeds and chariot through the mellay straight.*
> *Great though thou art, I would not, as in fear,*
> *Stealthily strike thee, but with open blow.*

As he spoke, Hector balanced his spear in his hand and flung it. It struck Ajax's massive shield on its outer bronze layer and pierced through six layers of hide, but then stuck fast. Ajax then threw his spear which went through Hector's shield and through his ornate body armor too. But Hector dodged just in time to avoid the blow

ARMOR AS LOOT

THE ARMOR WORN BY WARRIORS ON BOTH SIDES WAS OFTEN BEAUTIFULLY WROUGHT AND PATTERNED, SOMETIMES EVEN MADE OF GOLD, AND BY FAR THE MOST VALUABLE ASSET THEY POSSESSED. WHEN THE HEROES FOUGHT AND KILLED THEIR OPPONENTS, THEY WON HONOR ON THE BATTLEFIELD, BUT AS A RECOGNITION OF THAT THERE WAS THE ADDED PRIZE OF TAKING THEIR VICTIMS' ARMOR AS A TROPHY—IF THEY COULD GET AWAY WITH IT IN THE HEAT OF BATTLE.

Hector and Ajax, both honorable men, fought as the champions of each side in a vain attempt to put an end to a war that had been caused by the bad behavior of the gods.

GREAT AJAX

THERE WERE TWO
WARRIORS CALLED
AJAX ON THE GREEK
SIDE. "GREAT" AJAX
WAS THE BIGGER OF
THE TWO, AND
IMMENSELY STRONG.
HE WAS THE SON OF
TELAMON, LED THE
FLEET OF SHIPS FROM
SALAMIS, AND WAS
THE HERO CHOSEN
BY LOT BY HIS
COMRADES TO FIGHT
HECTOR IN SINGLE
COMBAT. AFTER THE
END OF THE BOOK,
THOUGH, HE WAS
DESTINED FOR
DISASTER—GOING
CRAZY AND KILLING
HIMSELF AFTER THE
DISHONOR OF BEING
REFUSED THE ARMOR
OF THE DEAD
ACHILLES.

and it merely ripped the cloth of his tunic. The two then retrieved their spears and attacked each other at close quarters. Hector's spear was bent by Ajax's shield, but again Ajax managed to pierce Hector's shield, grazing his neck. Blood began to trickle, then pour down the Trojan's side.

Hector bent down and grabbed a jagged piece of rock from the ground, and flung it at Ajax. It hit the boss of his shield with a great clang. Ajax then picked up a bigger rock and hurled it at Hector, knocking him off his feet. The rock stove in his shield, which fell on top of him. Apollo rushed down and lifted Hector back up again, but before they could do each other any more injury, two men from each side, Talthybius and Idaeus, stepped forward and leaped between the two warriors. They urged the two to break off the fight before it got dark, because they had both proved themselves fine spearmen and beloved of Zeus.

Ajax replied that Hector had to call off the fight, because it had been his challenge. Hector was in a chivalrous mood, and said that Ajax had shown himself the best spearman on the Greek side. He agreed to bring the duel to an end:

> *The night is falling; yield we unto night.*
> *Depart in peace, and cheer Achaia's host,*
> *Thine own kin and thy comrades, most of all.*
> *I too within King Priam's citadel*
> *Will cheer the Trojans, and their long-robed wives,*
> *Who now are thronging for my sake their shrines.*
> *But let us give each other gifts of mark,*
> *That men in either host may see, and say:*
> *"They fought together for their rivalry,*
> *Like friends at eve they parted, and in peace."*

As he said this, Hector took off his silver-riveted sword, together with its scabbard and belt and gave it to Ajax; Ajax gave him his purple belt. Bearing their gifts, they returned to their own lines, where they were greeted with delight by their fellow soldiers. Agamemnon sacrificed a bull to Zeus, then the Greeks began to feast and drink.

Once they had settled down to eat, Nestor made a speech. He said that they had suffered heavy losses and suggested that the Greeks should announce a truce at dawn. They could then bring the dead from the battle and burn them near the ships so that the bones could be taken home to their children. Nestor also counseled that the Greeks should build walls to protect the ships, with gates big enough to allow chariots through, and a ditch to protect the walls. Everyone agreed with the plan.

A truce is called

Meanwhile, in Priam's palace, the Trojans were having a confused and nervous meeting. Antenor claimed that it was time that the Trojans gave back Helen together with all Menelaus' property that came with her. Paris retorted that he would never give up his wife, but conceded that the treasure she had brought with her should be returned, and that he would add something of his own as well.

Priam acceded to this proposal, and suggested that they also ask for a truce to bury the dead. At dawn, Priam's messenger Idaeus went down to the Greek fleet to make the offer. Diomedes immediately urged his fellow leaders to reject it. The Trojans were doomed, and the Greeks had no need to accept any peace offering. His fellows shouted back their agreement, and Agamemnon gave his formal answer to Idaeus:

> With thine own ears, Idaeus, hast thou heard
> The answer that Achaia sends you back.
> Me too, their King, this pleaseth. For the dead—
> I grudge not that ye make their funeral due:
> Past are the dead; and who from harmless shades
> Would hinder the sweet offices of fire?
> Let then the Lord of thunder, Zeus supreme,
> Herè's great spouse, be witness to our truce.

So Idaeus returned with the rejection of Paris' offer, but an agreement to the truce to bury the dead. Greeks and Trojans were soon busying themselves with the funerals for the dead of the day before. So mutilated were the bodies that it was difficult to recognize them until the dried blood had been washed from their faces. The corpses were loaded onto wagons with much weeping. Priam had forbidden the Trojans to lament aloud, so they placed their dead onto the pyre in silence and went home to the city. The Greeks also burned their fallen comrades and returned to their ships.

Before dawn the next day, the Greek soldiers gathered around the smoldering funeral pyre and covered it with earth to make one huge communal grave. Then, as Nestor had suggested, they built walls against it to protect the ships, together with gates and a ditch guarded with a row of stakes.

As both sides feasted magnificently that night, the thunder echoed ominously down from heaven. Listening to Zeus' anger, soldiers from both sides turned pale and poured their wine from their cups on the ground as a libation to the gods.

Book 8
ZEUS FAVORS THE TROJANS

The rage of Zeus

INSTANT *ILIAD*

ZEUS, KING OF THE GODS, HAMMERS HOME HIS ABSOLUTE RULE ON OLYMPUS, AND FACES DOWN THE OTHER GODS WHEN THEY OPPOSE HIS PLAN; HE IS DETERMINED TO FULFILL HIS PROMISE TO THETIS, AND LET THE TROJANS GET THE BETTER OF THE BATTLE UNTIL THE FIGHTING REACHES THE BEACH, THE SHIPS, AND ULTIMATELY, ACHILLES. HUBRIS RULES AS HECTOR AND THE TROJANS THINK THAT THE VICTORY IS IN THEIR POCKET BECAUSE ZEUS IS ON THEIR SIDE.

At dawn the next day, Zeus ordered the gods to meet on the peak of Olympus, where he harangued them with a bravura display of pre-emptive threats. He made it clear that he was king of the gods, that he could destroy them all on a whim, and that if any one of them even considered helping either the Greeks or the Trojans, he would whip them into submission or hurl them into Tartarus for dark eternity. No one was to interfere with his masterplan; and he dared them to test him if they thought he was bluffing:

> Nay, put me to the proof, if ye so list:
> Suspend from heaven a golden chain, and lay,
> Gods, Goddesses, together, hands thereon;
> Not with your utmost labour shall ye draw
> The Lord of counsel earthward from the skies;
> But, let me will to draw it strenuously,
> I draw it up, and with it earth and sea,
> Enwind it round Olympus' summit fast,
> And all the world suspended hangs in air.
> So far o'er God and man I rise supreme.

The gods sat petrified with fear and astonishment. Finally Athena spoke up. She said that none of them would dream of opposing Zeus, they all knew it would be pointless. Nevertheless, she added daringly, they were all sad to see the gallant Greeks dying in such agony, and such numbers, to fulfill destiny's demands. Athena proposed that she and the other gods would offer military and tactical advice, with Zeus' agreement, so that there would not be a total Greek massacre. Zeus beamed brightly at his favorite daughter and reassured her that he had no intention of carrying out his threats (although he clearly did), and that he loved her dearly.

Then Zeus put on his golden armor, and took up his golden, coiling whip, leaped aboard his chariot, and lashed his bronze-hoofed horses across the skies toward Mount Ida. From his great mountain-top throne on the peak called Gargara he had a grandstand seat, looking down on the entire field of battle from the walls of Troy to the line of Greek ships along the sea's edge.

PLACES OF THE GODS

ALL THE MAJOR GODS EXCEPT HADES AND POSEIDON LIVED ON MOUNT OLYMPUS, IN HUGE GLITTERING HALLS BUILT FOR THEM BY HEPHAESTUS. OLYMPUS, ON THE EASTERN SIDE OF MAINLAND GREECE, ALMOST DIRECTLY FACED TROY. ZEUS SPENT A LOT OF HIS TIME ON TOP OF MOUNT IDA, THE HIGHEST PEAK OF THE REGION AROUND TROY, WHERE HE COULD GET A GOOD VIEW OF THE BATTLEFIELD. ANOTHER FAVORED PLACE WAS SAMOTHRACE, AN ISLAND IN THE NORTH EASTERN AEGEAN. POSEIDON WENT TO THIS ISLAND TO GET AN OVERVIEW OF THE WAR.

The Greek and Trojan armies met, and began slaughtering each other. The Iliad *was very specific about what happened to human flesh when it was run through by spears and swords, and warriors on both sides suffered terrible death agonies.*

The scales are tipped

In their camp, the Greeks threw on their armor as they ate; in the city, the Trojans geared up too. There were fewer of them, but they were more determined—they had wives and children to fight for. The city gates were flung open and the Trojan army surged out. The armies clashed head to head in noise and confusion, shields slamming, pikes and spears clashing against each other, men screaming in brutal triumph or death agony; the earth shook as men fought and killed or were killed, and their blood flowed like libations to the gods. The battle raged all morning, with huge losses on both sides.

Zeus watched the fighting intently; then, at noon, he took action. Into each pan of his golden scales he cast a fate—one for the Greeks, one for the Trojans. Then he held the scales aloft so that the sun glared off the bright gold. Slowly, the pan with the Greeks' fate in it sank, and the Trojans' fate rose. Zeus hurled a huge thunderbolt down on the Greek forces; every soldier trembled before the god's ferocious power.

Diomedes' dilemma

Even the Greek heroes, seasoned campaigners, were unmanned: Idomeneus, Agamemnon, and both the Ajaxes. They turned and ran. Old Nestor stood his ground, but that was only because Paris had killed one of his horses, and the rest of the team were plunging about in panic. Even as Nestor hacked desperately at the traces trying to cut the horses loose, Hector was driving down on him, and would have killed him if Diomedes had not noticed; he screamed at Odysseus, who was nearer, to come and help:

> *Odysseus, heavenly-born, Laertes' Son!*
> *Whither like any craven in the rout*
> *Fleest thou with face dishonourably turn'd?*
> *See lest a spear should pierce thee in the back!*
> *Nay, turn, and from this Savage save our sire!*

But Odysseus, oblivious, was running away, so Diomedes, driving the team of Trojan horses he had plundered from Aeneas, charged alone to the front, pulling up in front of Nestor, and plucking him from his useless chariot. Diomedes flung the reins at Nestor, urging him to drive so he could concentrate on the fighting. Nestor grabbed them, and at once they were charging toward Hector. Diomedes flung his spear which missed Hector but hit his driver, who fell screaming from the chariot. Hector could not stop, and trampled over the body of his friend, desperate for a new driver.

Seeing that things were not going all Hector's way, Zeus struck quickly. A blaze of white lightning split the earth right in front of Diomedes' chariot; the horses reared in terror, Nestor lost the reins and realized at once that they were up against more than mere mortals; the god was not on their side. He begged Diomedes to retreat:

> *Let us away, Tydides!* Let us flee!*
> *Seest thou, no strength from Heav'n attends us here?*
> *The glory of this day doth Zeus vouchsafe*
> *Wholly to Hector, yet to us may turn,*
> *Hereafter, if he please: no man may bend,*
> *How strong soe'er he be, the mind of Zeus*
> *To his own side: for Zeus is mightier far.*

* *son of Tydeus, i.e. Diomedes*

The armies clashed head to head in noise and confusion.

NESTOR

However, Diomedes was having none of this; he knew that Nestor was right, but he hated to think that Hector would gloat about him if he turned back. It was more than his pride could bear:

> My Father, well and wisely hast thou said.
> But this the fear that stings me to the quick;
> Lest Hector boast in loud harangue to Troy,
> He drave Tydides frighted to their fleet;
> May I be in my grave ere this his boast!

Nestor, who had grown older and wiser because he understood that part of valor that involved discretion, wrestled with the reins, while he tried to persuade Diomedes to turn back. Let Hector boast; no one, not even a Trojan, would believe that Diomedes was a coward, least of all the widows and orphans whose husbands and fathers he had slaughtered. Finally, Nestor managed to turn the horses, wrenched the chariot around, and started back toward the Greek lines, dodging a hail of Trojan spears and pursued by a triumphant Hector, screaming the very taunts that Diomedes feared:

> Hence, hence, Tydides! Whom above thy peers
> By seat and choicest viands and full cups
> The Danaans still have lifted, but henceforth
> Shall hold in mere dishonour, like a girl!

The wretched Diomedes was torn in two; should he turn and face down Hector? Or should he stay cool, follow Nestor's advice and live to fight another day? Three times he turned back, but each time Zeus sent down an earth-scorching thunderbolt that cut him off. Hector realized that Zeus was favoring the Trojans, and knew that he had to seize the time. He rallied his troops, whooping with joy:

> Trojans and Lycians! Dardan men-at-arms!
> Be men, my friends, and mindful of your might.
> Full well I know that Zeus hath will'd this day
> To me great glory, to the Danaans hurt.

Hector was a man possessed; nothing could hold him back, he would fight past the Greeks' paltry defensive ditch to the ships, and he would burn them. And he charged after Nestor and Diomedes, intent on seizing their armor and humiliating them entirely.

Hera fights back

Up on Olympus, Hera was beside herself. She screamed in the face of the luckless Poseidon, Zeus' brother, god of the oceans. Had he no pity for the dying Greeks? The people who honored him with shiploads of gifts and sacrifice at every port? Where was his gratitude? She urged the other gods to help her—if they all worked together, they could oppose Zeus' will; he was only one god, after all:

> *If all who love their cause, together strove*
> *Zeus to oppose and drive the Trojans back,*
> *On Ida He might gnash his teeth in vain.*

Poseidon was horrified. He was not about to cross Zeus. Nor were any other Olympians. The god was far too strong. Hera fumed in impotent rage and turned her thoughts to alternative strategies.

On the battlefield, Hector and his Trojans had driven the Greeks back entirely. Hector would have reached the Greek ships and destroyed them if Hera had not entered Agamemnon's heart and inspired him. His scarlet cloak billowing, the king ran to the ships, scrambled up onto the great black hull that belonged to Odysseus, and stood high on the stern where everyone could see and hear him. He tried to shame his troops into action, accusing them of bluster and brag and empty boasts, and abject cringing before just one man:

> *Shame on you! Valiant to the eye alone,*
> *Argeians, vile reproaches to the name!*
> *Where now the windy threat'nings, and the vaunts*
> *That dubb'd us bravest of the brave, what time,*
> *In Lemnos feasting full on flesh of ox,*
> *Crowning our cups with wine, we held high talk*
> *How each against his hundreds here in Troy*
> *Would stand victorious? Yet doth one man's arm*
> *Outmatch us all, and Hector fires our ships.*

Agamemnon wept, and prayed aloud to Zeus, reminding him of all the sacrifices he had made in Zeus' many shrines. He did not ask for victory, just for his men to escape with their lives, and not drown ignominiously in a bloodbath.

Agamemnon wept, and prayed aloud to Zeus.

Zeus listened, and pitied, and made a decision; he could preserve the Greeks from utter massacre and still keep his promise to Thetis. Pleased with this neat solution, he sent a sign—an eagle clutching a fawn—to acknowledge the Greeks' prayers.

Battle renewed

Zeus' sign instantly rekindled the Greeks' fighting spirit. They rallied, and flung themselves on the Trojans. None was more aflame with battle lust than Diomedes; he was the first to draw Trojan blood. Driving recklessly to the defensive trench, he brought down Argelaus, just as the Trojan was wrenching his chariot around to turn and flee. Where Diomedes carved a way through the Trojan ranks, Agamemnon, Menelaus, Idomeneus, and the Ajaxes followed; hidden behind Great Ajax's shield crept Teucer, the sniper, slotting shots through his own ranks and decimating the Trojans. Many of the bravest Trojans were felled, one after the other, by Teucer's deadly, silent shafts. His main target was Hector, but time and again, he missed him, as the archer god Apollo deflected his arrows. One killed Hector's charioteer, so the Trojan leaped down, seized a jagged rock and went for Teucer before he could notch another arrow, smashing his right shoulder. Ajax instantly covered the wounded marksman with his shield and helped to scramble him out of the battle and back to the safety of the ships.

Zeus may have granted that the Greeks would not be massacred, but he was still intent on getting the Trojans to their ships. Inspired by Zeus, Hector led the charge, once again driving the Greeks back relentlessly behind their defenses, hacking down stragglers as they fled. He drove his chariot right up to the edge of the defensive rampart, shouting in triumph as his enemies melted before him.

TEUCER

THE GREEK'S CRACK ARCHER, TEUCER, WAS THE BASTARD SON OF TELAMON AND HESIONE, DAUGHTER OF LAOMEDON AND SISTER OF PRIAM, KING OF TROY. TEUCER THEREFORE HAD DIVIDED LOYALTIES, BUT CHOSE TO FIGHT WITH THE GREEKS, ALONGSIDE HIS HALF BROTHER GREAT AJAX, SHARING HIS SHIELD.

Hera and Athena

On Olympus, Hera was once more filled with anger and pity. Hector was again mowing down her darling boys. She turned to Athena, begging her to help:

Can we, great child of Zeus, behold unmoved
The Danaans falling in this need extreme?
All doom'd they perish by the stormy hand
Of this one man, ev'n Hector, Priam's son.

Athena's blood boiled, but not entirely out of pity for the Greek fighters. She was mortified that her father had turned his heart against her, and ragingly jealous of Thetis, who had charmed a promise out of him. Her mind gnawed away at all the times she had helped Zeus out—especially with Heracles, his wretched trouble-magnet of a son—and now she was being sidelined just because Zeus was bedazzled by a silly little sea nymph. Surely the sight of her and Hera, fully armed, would make him think twice? The two goddesses buckled up into their armor, climbed into Hera's chariot, and charged toward the gates of Olympus.

However, over on Mount Ida, Zeus had seen them. He was furious. Summoning his messenger Iris, he ordered her to go and stop the rebellious pair, and threaten them with his vengeance. Iris was to outline in forensic detail what would happen to them if they persisted, and there was a particular message for Athena:

Under the wheels their coursers I will maim,
Dash down themselves, and shatter all their car;
Nor shall ten circling years make whole the wounds

IRIS

THE GODDESS OF THE RAINBOW, THE PHENOMENON THAT APPEARS TO CONNECT EARTH TO THE HEAVENS, IRIS WAS THE SPECIAL MESSENGER OF ZEUS, TAKING HIS DISPATCHES TO AND FROM MOUNT IDA AND OLYMPUS, AND THE BATTLEFIELD, WHERE SHE OFTEN DISGUISED HERSELF AS A MORTAL.

Wherewith my thunderbolts shall scathe them sore.
So shall the bright-eyed Maiden rue the day
Of combat with her Father.

Iris caught up with the pair before they had even left Olympus, and passed on Zeus' message word for word. Hera caved in instantly. They should turn back, and not fight with Zeus, not for the sake of mere men. Let Zeus decide the fates of both Greeks and Trojans; his plan must prevail:

I would not that for mortals' sake we stand
'Gainst Zeus in single battle: as may hap,
Let one man die, and let another live,
Whilst He, according to his own sage plans,
Awards to either side what seemeth good.

Slowly she turned the chariot round and the goddesses slunk back into Olympus, all the heart gone out of them.

Lucky that they did. As soon as Iris had been dispatched, Zeus leaped onto his chariot and galloped back to Olympus in person. The ground shook as he strode into the hall and flung himself onto his great throne. Hera and Athena sat apart, in dignified silence. As they did not speak to him, he began to goad them. He hoped they were not too worn out after all that heroic fighting and slaughtering of Trojans; but then, they were too scared to actually venture onto a battlefield, weren't they? The goddesses seethed. Athena was wise enough just to smolder resentfully in silence, but Hera, as usual, could not contain herself. She was still angry and she still wanted to help the Greeks. Zeus merely scoffed at her. If she wanted to try, she would get her chance the very next day: she could advise the Greeks while he slaughtered them—it was his will that Hector should triumph until Achilles was provoked enough to join in battle:

... Nor shall cease
Hector triumphant, ere the fleetfoot Son
Of Peleus* rise uproused amongst the ships,
On that dread day, when at the galleys' sterns
In direst strait above Patroclus' corpse
The hosts have met. This, this is heaven's decree ...
* i.e. Achilles

> *It was his will that Hector should triumph until Achilles was provoked enough to join the battle.*

Hera could be as angry as she liked but it made no difference—his will would prevail. The Queen of Olympus sat silent, not daring to reply. And the sun went down on Zeus' anger. On the battlefield, the Trojans resented the dying of the light—they wanted to press home their victory; but the Greeks welcomed night as a blessed relief.

Hector rallies the troops

Hector pulled back his troops, mustering them on open ground near the river. They got down from their chariots and gathered around him. Leaning on his great spear he gave his orders, explained battle tactics for the following day, and offered his own prayers to Zeus. He had hoped to have finished off the Greeks, and to be returning to Troy in triumph by now, but the coming of night had saved the enemy. So the Trojans would rest and eat and feed their stalwart horses; but there were to be watchfires set so they could see if the Greeks tried to cut and run under cover of darkness, to get away scot-free. Hector wanted every last Greek to carry with him a wound, a souvenir from Troy, a health warning for anyone else thinking they might take on the Trojans:

> *Ne'er be it said that unassail'd, unscathed,*
> *They so departed: rather, when they feel*
> *Hereafter at their own firesides the smart*
> *Of the old wounds we scarr'd them ere they sail'd,*
> *Others shall see and fear, and lay to heart*
> *That warning of the mighty men of Troy.*

And the city itself had to be defended. Hector sent orders for all the old men and boys too young to fight to set a ring of tents around the city walls, and light sentry fires. In their homes, women should light bright fires on the hearth. The city's night watch should be extra vigilant. They would fight again at daybreak; for himself, he planned an early grudge match with Diomedes, imagining his enemy's blood staining the earth red just as the rising sun stains the sky.

Filled with enthusiasm, his iron-hearted Trojans cheered their commander. Spirits were high as they made camp; a thousand watch fires burned in the still night air, as bright and constant as the stars; around each one sat 50 men, their horses quietly champing barley by their side. So the Trojans waited for dawn and victory.

Book 9
PLEADING WITH ACHILLES

The despair of the Greeks

The Greeks did not share the calm certainty of their Trojan opponents. Panic, alarm, and despondency swept through their camp. Even Agamemnon felt icy despair grip his heart, but he walked among the men with his heralds calling the troops and their officers to a muster. They huddled around the meeting ground, disconsolate. Agamemnon rose to speak, the tears running down his bleak cheeks. He blamed Zeus for their predicament; Zeus who had promised him Troy, but had obviously gone back on his word. And in a doleful echo of the ill-advised speech he had made to test his soldiers' loyalty, he again urged them to give up and go home:

> Then hear me, and obey, as I give word.
> Let us away to our dear fatherland;
> Flee; for broad-streeted Troy will ne'er be ours.

For a long time, no one answered him—they were too far sunk in gloom. It was the impetuous Diomedes who finally spoke. Claiming the customary right of free speech and immunity from reprisals during official assemblies, he tore into Agamemnon. The king had once called him a coward, but he liked to think he had proved otherwise. Now it was his turn to call out Agamemnon, whom the gods had only half blessed: they had granted him the scepter of honor but withheld the courageous spirit needed to wield it. Why did Agamemnon believe that all men were as tiny-hearted as he was?

> Thine is the sceptre of the throne supreme,
> Not thine the valorous heart—the soul of power.
> Oh, couldst thou deem, dear Lord, Achaia's sons

Such skulks and cowards (it is thine own fair word)
As to accept this counsel? Flee thyself,
If thy heart prompts thee ...

Agamemnon could desert if he wanted to—the sea lanes were undefended—but his armies would stay and fight until they had plundered Troy; and even if they ran, Diomedes himself would fight until the bitter end. Had Agamemnon forgotten that it was the gods who had sent them on this mission?

The troops cheered Diomedes on, but Nestor, sensing impending mutiny, quickly rose to pour his own brand of soothing oil on troubled waters. He praised Diomedes for his forthright and manly speech—who could not agree with every word he said, so young and yet so wise—nevertheless, ranting would get them nowhere. He was older than Diomedes, and by implication wiser; he suggested that they take advantage of the night and the lull in fighting to regroup; the men could eat and rest; and Agamemnon could host a feast for the senior chiefs—that would at least be a duty within his grasp. After the feast, everyone could have their say, and they would decide what to do. The enemy was sniffing around their tent-flaps; it was time to act.

Relieved to have been given a practical direction at last, the soldiers acted on Nestor's suggestion. Watchfires were lit and over 700 sentries placed on guard.

Panic, alarm, and despondency swept through the Greek camp.

Agamemnon's feast

At Agamemnon's tents, the king had commanded a great feast—the Greeks had unlimited access to wine and fine food, delivered daily by ships from Thrace. When the captains had eaten and drunk their fill, Nestor stood up to offer his advice. Although he took care to flatter Agamemnon, he also made it very clear that it was the king's duty to follow the best advice on offer—namely Nestor's. For a career diplomat, he did not mince words. Everything had gone wrong since Agamemnon, against sage counsel, had so enraged Achilles and driven him away. It was never a good idea to cross those whom the gods love best, but even now maybe it was not too late to make amends and bring the great warrior around:

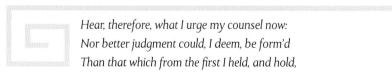

Hear, therefore, what I urge my counsel now:
Nor better judgment could, I deem, be form'd
Than that which from the first I held, and hold,

AGAMEMNON'S GIFTS

TO PERSUADE HIM TO FIGHT, AGAMEMNON PROMISED THESE GIFTS TO ACHILLES:
❖ SEVEN TRIPODS (TRADITIONALLY PRIZED POSSESSIONS, CARRYING RITUAL SIGNIFICANCE; OFTEN GIVEN AS TROPHIES).
❖ TEN BARS OF GOLD.
❖ TWENTY BURNISHED CAULDRONS.
❖ A DOZEN RACING STALLIONS.
❖ SEVEN BEAUTIFUL WOMEN FROM LESBOS.
❖ THE GIRL BRISEIS, WHOM AGAMEMNON HAD STOLEN FROM ACHILLES, AND A SOLEMN OATH THAT HE HAD NEVER TOUCHED HER.
❖ AS MUCH PLUNDER FROM TROY AS ACHILLES' SHIPS COULD HOLD.
❖ 20 OF THE MOST BEAUTIFUL TROJAN WOMEN.
❖ ANY ONE OF AGAMEMNON'S THREE BEAUTIFUL DAUGHTERS AS A BRIDE, WITH A DOWRY OF SEVEN SEPARATE CITADELS.

Ev'n from the hour when, with a forceful hand,
Thou bar'st the maid Briseis from the tent
Of Peleus' Son,* and leftest him in wrath—
Not by our counsel; I forbade the act
With much dissuasion—nathless, under sway
Of thine own haughty temper, thou durst do
To him dishonour, whom the Immortal Gods
Delight to honour most, the first of men ...

* Peleus' son, i.e. Achilles

Agamemnon was abjectly, hair-tearingly contrite. Nestor was quite right. He must have been mad to alienate the one fighter who could save the Greeks:

Not false the count, my father, thou has made
Of these my fell transgressions; I have err'd
Greatly, nor I myself deny my sin.

Now Agamemnon was just as manically keen to give back Briseis—and to swear an oath that he had not touched her—and to smother Achilles in gifts of treasure, horses, women, and land as he had been determined to swindle and disgrace the great warrior previously. Even so, he could not resist boasting of his own generosity. No one could accuse Agamemnon of pinching the pennies—he would pile all this upon Achilles if only the recalcitrant warrior, more unforgiving than the god of death himself, would rise above his rage and come back and fight with the hard-pressed Greeks. But Agamemnon could not quite abase himself; he still wanted Achilles to acknowledge that he was king:

All this will I perform, if he relent.
Let him yield therefore, and be turn'd from wrath;
Hades alone is unpropitiable,
Alone unyielding, and, for this same cause,
Is loathed by mortals most of all the Gods.
He well may yield to me, who am of race
More royal, and may boast me more in years.

While Agamemnon was still hot from high-toned rhetoric and filled with awe at his own generosity, Nestor seized the moment. Envoys had to be sent immediately to take Agamemnon's offer to Achilles and try to persuade him to come back with them. Nestor suggested they should send three: Odysseus (usually able to talk anybody into anything), Great Ajax (the second greatest Greek warrior after Achilles), and Phoenix (the old soldier who had helped raise Achilles and taught him most of what he knew about fighting). Before Agamemnon could start regretting his dramatic promises, Nestor called for wine and water, prayers were made to Zeus, and the negotiating party set off, Phoenix going ahead with two heralds to lead the way.

Achilles, unarmed for war, sat by his ships brooding obsessively about how shamelessly Agamemnon had treated him.

At Achilles' tent

With last-minute advice from Nestor ringing in their ears, Odysseus and Ajax set off, trudging along the seashore beside the crashing breakers, each praying as hard as he could to Zeus that they could soften Achilles' heart.

Inside Achilles' tent, the scene could not have been more calm and peaceful, light years from the dust, blood, and carnage that the battle-weary Greeks were used to. Achilles sat plucking his lyre, singing songs of ancient heroes and old glories; and with him sat Patroclus, listening in rapt silence. When Odysseus and Ajax came into the tent, Achilles leaped to his feet in surprise, but greeted them warmly as old, true friends. He sat them down on rich cushioned chairs, ordered Patroclus to bring more wine, and bustled about chopping and cooking meat, fetching bread, and setting out a huge feast on the table. Before they could explain why they had come, Odysseus, Ajax, and Phoenix had to tackle their second banquet of the evening. When they had eaten enough, Ajax gave a nod to Phoenix to start the discussion, but it was Odysseus who took the hint; refilling his wine cup, he lifted it in a toast to Achilles' health, and got down to business.

Odysseus pulled no punches; he told Achilles exactly what the military situation was. The Greeks were pinned back against their own ships, surrounded by Trojan camps. At dawn, the enemy would attack. What was more, Zeus appeared to be on the Trojans' side, so Hector believed himself invincible. He intended to burn the ships and kill every last Greek, and Odysseus was terrified that Zeus would make it so. He urged Achilles, man to man, to get into gear and come and help while there was still time, just. Surely he would not want to let down his brothers-in-arms?

ODYSSEUS

THE SON OF LAERTES AND KING OF ITHACA. HE HAD DONE HIS BEST NOT TO GET INVOLVED IN THE TROJAN ADVENTURE, BUT WAS IN THE END FORCED TO HONOR THE OATH HE HAD SUGGESTED TO HELEN'S FATHER. ODYSSEUS WAS THE CLEVEREST STRATEGIST IN THE GREEK ARMY, OBVIOUSLY A FAVORITE OF THE RANK AND FILE, AND WAS UNAFRAID TO CHALLENGE AGAMEMNON'S JUDGMENT. ALTHOUGH MORE BRAINS THAN BRAWN, HE WAS ALSO A GOOD FIGHTER, AND SPECIALIZED IN STEALTH OPERATIONS. IT WAS ODYSSEUS WHO DEVISED THE TROJAN HORSE AND LED THE TROOP OF WARRIORS WITHIN IT.

> *... Oh then rise!*
> *Surely thyself desirest, in this sore need,*
> *Though late, to save thy country! Else, be sure,*
> *Bitter hereafter will they sorrows be,*
> *When all is past; past evil hath no cure.*
> *Now therefore, whilst time serves, resolve how best*
> *To save the Danaans from this evil hour.*

Without waiting for a reaction to this simple, straight-from-the-heart appeal, Odysseus brought Achilles' father, Peleus, into the argument; surely Achilles remembered how his father had begged him, when he sent him off to join Agamemnon's forces, to try to keep his raging pride under control:

> *Ah friend! Thy father Peleus, on the day*
> *He sent thee forth from Phthia to the King,*
> *Oft charged thee thus: "My child, if so they will,*
> *Pallas* and Herè may vouchsafe thee strength;*
> *But keep the high, haught spirit in thy breast*
> *Well-govern'd: kindness is the better part,*
> *To cease from evil rancour; and the host,*
> *Both young and old, shall honour thee the more."*
> * Pallas = Athena

Pleading with Achilles to relent, to let his soul-sapping anger go, Odysseus wheeled on the big guns; he told Achilles about all the treasure that Agamemnon had offered, in the hearing of the entire Greek army, and that he would give back Briseis together with a sworn oath that he had not touched her. They were all Achilles' for the taking. Then Odysseus played one of his wily mindgames; he was blunt with Achilles, a fellow soldier—perhaps Agamemnon's fawning generosity sickened him, and made him loathe the king even more; perhaps he resented the implication that he could be bought; but would he not think about coming back for the sake of his comrades, or if not that, for the honor and lasting glory of killing the great Hector?

Achilles listened in silence to this masterly piece of manipulative persuasion. Then he spoke. He was going to speak plainly, telling them straight out what he felt in his heart, because he loathed people who said one thing but thought another; and what he had to tell them, he hoped, would stop them from pestering him.

Agamemnon would never, ever win him over, nor would any other Greek Agamemnon sent. Where was all this concern when he was hacking his way through enemy soldiers just to get plunder for Agamemnon, skulking in his ship, well out of danger? When he risked his neck plundering the 12 cities they attacked on the voyage to Troy, only to find that all the spoils had gone to the king, who had shared them out with everybody, coward and hero alike, and given back so little to the man who had won them? The only sure reward of war was death:

> *For when I battled without rest or pause*
> *Against their foes, they render'd me no grace.*
> *Like shares to all—the lingerer in the camp*
> *And him who fought his utmost; best and worst*
> *Stood in one estimation; cravens vile*
> *And men most staunch show'd equal in their deaths.*

And Achilles returned again and again to Briseis; the shameless Agamemnon had taken her, disgracing Achilles in front of everybody. Achilles had loved Briseis just as much as Menelaus loved Helen—and they had all gone to war just because someone had taken Helen—yet no one would fight with him to get her back:

> *Never was true man yet, or sound of heart,*
> *But loved and cherish'd to himself his own;*
> *As I from my inmost soul loved her,*

Agamemnon would never win him over, nor would any other Greek.

He wasn't fighting ever again; he planned to set sail at dawn.

Slave though she be, and captive of my spear.
Yet he tore her away. And dares he now
Entreat me? Nay, he hath beguiled me once;
I read him through and through; 'tis waste of breath.

Agamemnon should find some other way out of his own mess; after all, he had managed to build a ditch and a rampart, although it hadn't held Hector back. When Achilles had been fighting, great Hector would not have dared come so close to the Greek camps; but he wasn't fighting now, and he no longer wanted to kill Hector. In fact, he wasn't fighting ever again; he planned to set sail at dawn—everybody was welcome to come and see him off if they had time and inclination. He would pick up the booty he had left and go home to Phthia. He told Odysseus to take his message to Agamemnon, and shout it aloud out in the open, so everyone could hear, and no one else would be taken in by the shameless king:

... Wherefore tell him all,
Ev'n in my own words, and in public place,
That others too may chafe against his craft,
Forewarn'd, if haply he be plotting there,
Cloak'd in the shamelessness he ever wears,
Some Danaans more to cozen: in my face,
Dog though he be, he would not dare to look!
I will not share his counsel nor his works:
He hath deceived and wrong'd me once; again
He shall not with these glozing words: enough—
And let him to his ruin clear of me!
Zeus hath bereft him of his better sense.

Achilles did not stop there. He sneered at the gifts Agamemnon had offered: there was simply not enough treasure, horseflesh, or beautiful women in the world to make up for what Agamemnon had done, not even if his gifts had outnumbered all the grains of sand in the world. He would never marry one of Agamemnon's daughters, not if she were as beautiful as Aphrodite and as skilled as Athena. He wanted to settle down with a local bride for a life of peaceful contentment. Agamemnon wanted to buy Achilles' life with untold wealth, but his life was not for sale any more, and he no longer wanted to wager it in paltry cattle raids for the benefit of paltry kings. Then Achilles revealed the prophecy made by his mother

Thetis: if he stayed to fight, he would die but be glorious ever after; if he left, he would live a long contented life, but unsung by any muse. Agamemnon's behavior had prompted him to choose the contentment route:

> *Two threads conduct me to the bourne of death:*
> *If I remain and battle on with Troy,*
> *Hope of return must perish, but my name*
> *Shall live for ever; if I get me hence*
> *And reach mine own dear fatherland again,*
> *My name shall perish, but my life shall be long,*
> *Nor death o'ertake me with an early end.*

He advised them all to take sail as well; Troy would never fall, not while Zeus defended it. Their embassy had been useless—the Greek chiefs would have to find some other way. Then Achilles invited Phoenix to stay the night, and sail with him in the morning, if he wanted.

Phoenix fails

It was a long speech. They were all stunned. Poor Phoenix, the old soldier, was so overcome that he burst into tears, afraid of what would happen to the Greeks without Achilles. He was in a terrible dilemma; he had been with Achilles, as mentor and teacher, since the warrior's babyhood. If Achilles was set on returning, and refused to save the Greeks, he would have to go with him:

> *If of a truth, thou star of men, thy heart*
> *Is altogether set on this return,*
> *And if though utterly refuse to save*
> *Achaia's galleys from these threatening fires,*
> *Yet how, dear child, may I be left by thee*
> *Forlorn behind?*

Phoenix tried to persuade Achilles to change his mind by reminding him of their life together, reminiscing about the baby Achilles, burping and bouncing on his knee. Achilles was like a son to him. He pleaded with him to unbend, to relent; if

PHOENIX

ACHILLES' TUTOR AND COMPANION, SENT TO TROY WITH ACHILLES BY PELEUS. AS A YOUTH, PHOENIX LEFT HIS OWN HOME IN HELLAS AFTER A TERRIBLE FEUD WITH HIS FATHER AMYNTOR. HIS MOTHER BEGGED HIM TO SEDUCE AMYNTOR'S YOUNG MISTRESS, AND HE DID SO, BUT HIS FATHER FOUND OUT AND CURSED HIM; HE WOULD NEVER FATHER A CHILD OF HIS OWN. SO HE RAN AWAY, EVENTUALLY COMING TO PHTHIA, WHERE KING PELEUS TOOK HIM IN, GAVE HIM A REGION TO RULE, AND ENTRUSTED HIM WITH THE UPBRINGING OF THE BABY ACHILLES, WHO BECAME LIKE A SON TO HIM.

Agamemnon had not offered all these gifts, Phoenix would be the first to condemn him, but he had, and sent Achilles' friends to plead his cause. Phoenix believed that Agamemnon had really repented of his disgraceful actions; he reminded Achilles of the cautionary tale of Meleager, another obdurate warrior whose recalcitrant pride led to tragedy. It would be harder to save the ships when they were burning—Achilles should fight now, while the gifts and treasure were on offer and the Achaeans would honor him like a god; if he left it too late, there would be no honor and no reward, and Phoenix hated to think of his protégé being so unlucky:

> *Come rather now, whilst gifts attend the help;*
> *Achaia now would grace thee like some God:*
> *But if hereafter, in thine own behalf,*
> *Losing these gifts, thou yet comest forth at last,*
> *Albeit thine arm be powerful as of old*
> *To save us, yet thy glory will be less.*

In spite of embarrassing revelations about his early years, Achilles was courteous, but firm with his old teacher. Why should he need honor from the troops? What Zeus had decreed was honor enough for him. Yet he showed his anger by warning Phoenix not to upset him any more by weeping and wailing on Agamemnon's account, otherwise he might come to hate his old friend. Achilles wanted Phoenix on his side, and once again asked him to stay the night and they could decide in the morning whether they would sail back to Greece or not.

The last throw

Ajax and Odysseus stood up to leave. Ajax had not yet spoken; now he played their last card. He was matter-of-fact. There was no point in staying, as Achilles was not going to change his mind—it would be better to get back, tell everybody the bad news, and start planning alternative strategies with the other chiefs:

> *Odysseus! Let us go. I see no end*
> *Likely to be fulfill'd by all our speech.*
> *Remains for us to carry this reply,*
> *Good though it be not, to the Danaan chiefs ...*

MELEAGER'S STORY

PHOENIX TOLD THE STORY OF MELEAGER TO TRY TO PERSUADE ACHILLES TO FIGHT. MELEAGER WAS THE SON OF OENEUS, KING OF CALYDON, AND ALTHAEA. WHEN OENEUS FAILED TO MAKE ACCEPTABLE SACRIFICE TO ARTEMIS, SHE SENT A WILD BOAR TO RAVAGE HIS COUNTRY. MELEAGER CALLED ALL THE GREEK HEROES TO COME AND HUNT THE BOAR. ATALANTA THE HUNTRESS DREW FIRST BLOOD, BUT MELEAGER FINISHED THE BEAST OFF. THERE ENSUED A VIOLENT QUARREL...

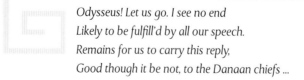

Then he rounded on Achilles, accusing him bluntly of abandoning his comrades, of being a hard, ruthless man, his heart stuffed with insatiable pride and anger, and all over just one girl. They could offer him seven such, and more beside. And Ajax pleaded with him one last time on behalf of the entire Greek army.

But Achilles was adamant; he would never forgive Agamemnon for treating him like a common tramp, mortifying him in front of everybody; yet he did offer a morsel of hope. He would fight, but only if Hector got as far as his own Myrmidon camp:

> *I will not give a thought how goes the fray,*
> *Till haply when great Hector, Priam's child,*
> *Gains in the onward path of slaughter borne*
> *The camp and fleet of these my Myrmidons,*
> *And threats with fire the galleys—then I trow,*
> *About my tent, at my black galley's side,*
> *Ev'n valorous Hector will perchance be stay'd.*

The envoys had to be content with that. The embassy was over. Phoenix stayed, but Odysseus and Ajax poured a libation to Zeus, then trudged off again, heavy-hearted, back down the beach to the Greek camp.

When they heard them coming back, Agamemnon and the other leaders leaped straight to their feet, jostling each other in order to get near them and pressing cups of wine on them, eager to hear the news. What had Achilles said? Would he fight? Did he refuse? Agamemnon was loudest of all. When the noise died down, Odysseus gave them the bad news. Achilles would not fight. They were on their own. Not only that, he had threatened to leave altogether—and he had advised everyone else to as well.

Deep gloom descended on the camp as Odysseus' black news sank in. There was a long silence; once again, it was the high-tempered Diomedes who broke it. He snarled that Agamemnon's efforts to buy him off with treasure had just made Achilles more proud than ever; he had had enough of Achilles—he would only fight when he felt like it—let him go or stay as he wanted. They didn't need him. They were on their own, they had to deal with the situation. They would be better off getting some sleep and making a battle plan in the morning, and Agamemnon could lead them into combat riding in the front rank.

Heartened by the indomitable Diomedes, the other captains rallied, poured a last libation to the gods, and retired to their tents to try to get some sleep.

MELEAGER'S STORY CONTINUED

AS MELEAGER WANTED TO GIVE ATALANTA A PRIZE, HE KILLED ONE OR BOTH OF HIS UNCLES, TOXEUS AND PLEXIPPUS. IN REVENGE, HIS MOTHER CURSED HIM, PRAYING THAT HE WOULD FALL IN BATTLE. SO WHEN THE CURETES ATTACKED CALYDON, MELEAGER REFUSED TO FIGHT, AND STAYED AT HOME IN BED. ONLY WHEN THE CITY WAS BURNING, AND HIS WIFE BEGGED HIM, WOULD HE GO OUT TO FIGHT, SAVING THE CITY IN TIME, BUT GETTING NO REWARD FOR HIS TROUBLE.

Book 10
SPIES AND NIGHTRAIDERS

Brothers-in-arms

INSTANT *ILIAD*

A SLEEPLESS
AGAMEMNON TRIES TO
WORK OUT WHAT TO
DO TO SAVE THE
GREEKS FROM
HECTOR'S RELENTLESS
ATTACK. HE DECIDES
TO SEND SPIES TO THE
TROJAN LINES. THE
TROJANS ALSO SEND
OUT A SPY, BUT HE IS
COWARDLY, AND NO
MATCH FOR ODYSSEUS
AND DIOMEDES, WHO
END THE NIGHT BY
MASSACRING AN
ENTIRE CONTINGENT
OF THRACIANS,
NEWLY ARRIVED
ALLIES OF TROY.

Despite their desperate situation, many of the Greek commanders managed to sleep through the night, but Agamemnon could get no rest. He stared hot-eyed at the distant Trojan fires, his heart leaden within him; and when he turned to survey the Greek ships clustering at the sea's very edge, fear gripped his soul and he paced about tearing his hair, groaning aloud and cursing Zeus. What was he to do? Eventually he decided to go and seek Nestor's advice, to see if they could come up with a last-minute life-saving strategy. Action was better than nail-biting. Agamemnon threw on his battle tunic, wrapped himself in a handsome lion's hide, grabbed his spear, and strode off toward Nestor's tent.

The same grim dread was wracking the soul of his brother Menelaus. He could not sleep either, tormented by the thought that his comrades, who had come to fight against Troy just for him, might all meet their end after sunrise, and their deaths would be held to his account. He also scrambled into his battle tunic and leopard-hide cloak, snatched his spear, and set out to Agamemnon's tent.

The brothers met beside Agamemnon's ship, and were pleased to see each other. As Agamemnon was strapping on the rest of his armor, Menelaus asked why he was arming up. Was he hoping to try to persuade someone to go and spy on the Trojan camp? If so, Menelaus did not hold out much hope:

> *Why arm'st thou thus, my Brother, at this hour?*
> *Wouldst prompt some chieftain forth to spy the foe?*
> *I fear for such a venture few thou'lt find.*
> *Bold must he be of heart, who dares go forth*
> *Alone through balmy darkness to their camp.*

Odysseus, the wily commando fighter, looks for spies and easy pickings in the night; he is wearing the boars' teeth helmet that once belonged to his grandfather.

Agamemnon, always the more forthright of the pair, replied that he was off to see Nestor to work out a plan to save their fleet and their men. The hard fact was Zeus had not only abandoned them, he had put all his power behind Hector. Agamemnon had never seen an ordinary mortal fight so fiercely and so well; there was grudging admiration as he spoke about their enemy who had caused such havoc:

> *Myself have ne'er*
> *With mine own eyes beheld, nor e'er heard tell,*
> *Such miracles of prowess by one man*
> *Achieved in battle, as by Hector wrought*
> *This day upon our host—albeit man mere,*
> *Not born of Goddess, nor by God begot;—*
> *Such deeds, I say, as Argos needs must rue*
> *For many a year; such evil hath he wrought.*

Agamemnon ordered Menelaus to go and rouse Great Ajax and Idomeneus, while he went to Nestor. He cautioned his brother to show some respect, to ask, not command— arrogance was not going to help them now. Zeus had been heaping hardships and indignities on them since they were born, and they needed all the help they could get.

ATRIDES

HOMER OFTEN
REFERRED TO THE
BROTHERS
AGAMEMNON AND
MENELAUS AS ATRIDES.
THIS WAS THEIR FAMILY
NAME, MEANING THAT
THEY WERE THE SONS
OF ATREUS, A KING
OF MYCENAE.

Waking the warriors

Agamemnon arrived outside Nestor's tent. The old man was sleeping, but lightly, like a battle-hardened old soldier, his armor polished and ready by his bed. As the king approached, Nestor sat up instantly and challenged him. Agamemnon responded. Did Nestor not recognize Agamemnon, the unluckiest man alive? Sleepless through fear and worry, he had come for counsel. He asked Nestor if he would get up and come with him to the sentry line to make sure that the guard had not fallen asleep and that the enemy were not poised to attack in the night.

Nestor did his best to prevent the king from sinking into paralyzing gloom. Hector would never triumph, he said stoutly; that was not Zeus' plan at all, and Hector would soon have troubles of his own if only Achilles would change his mind. Of course he would come with Agamemnon, and they should call out the other great captains— Odysseus, Idomeneus, the Ajaxes, and Meges. Nestor could not restrain himself from complaining about Menelaus, sleeping while his brother had to beg for help:

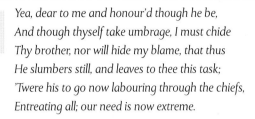

Yea, dear to me and honour'd though he be,
And though thyself take umbrage, I must chide
Thy brother, nor will hide my blame, that thus
He slumbers still, and leaves to thee this task;
'Twere his to go now labouring through the chiefs,
Entreating all; our need is now extreme.

Agamemnon leaped to his brother's defense. Agreed, Menelaus appeared to hang back, but he wasn't slack, it was just that he was waiting for his brother's command. Anyway, this time he had taken the initiative, and had come to Agamemnon, and now he had gone to rouse Great Ajax and Idomeneus.

Nestor got up, wrapped himself in a thick double cloak and, seizing his great bronze-tipped spear, he set off for Odysseus' tent, bellowing at him to wake up. Odysseus stumbled out of his tent, bellowing back. Who on earth was blundering about waking everyone up? Where was the fire? Nestor told him they were assembling a war council, so Odysseus went back into his tent, slung his great shield on his back, and joined the others, by now striding toward Diomedes' tent. They found him asleep on an oxhide bed, surrounded by his troops. Nestor lost no time, wading in with a kick in the ribs and a shout in the face. Diomedes started up, bleary with sleep and complaining; couldn't Nestor take a back seat for once? But he got up, slung his lion-hide around him, grasped his spear, and set off to rouse more men.

AIANTES

THIS IS THE COLLECTIVE NAME FOR THE TWO AJAXES, TELAMONIAN, OR GREAT AJAX (THE SON OF TELAMON) AND OILEAN, OR LITTLE AJAX (THE SON OF OÏLEUS). THEY WERE NOT RELATED.

Nestor's plan

The troop arrived at the sentry lines. Despite Agamemnon's fears, the guards were all wide awake—the enemy was so close that there was no danger of them closing their eyes for a second, and they started at every footstep. Much relieved, Nestor clambered across the Greek defensive trench. The other warriors followed him, and found a patch of clear ground, away from the mounds of corpses—the very spot where Hector had turned back his chariot, defeated by the failing light. They sat down side by side, and Nestor was first to put forward a plan. One of them should infiltrate the Trojan camp; perhaps they could kidnap a straggler, and force him to talk, or listen in unnoticed to the Trojan soldiers. They might pick up some vital information about the Trojan strategy—were they going to press on, or head home?

ODYSSEUS' HELMET

THIS WAS A STOUT , TIGHT-FITTING LEATHER HELMET, LINED WITH FELT AND REINFORCED ON THE OUTSIDE WITH ROWS OF GLEAMING WHITE BOARS' TEETH. THE HELMET HAD BEEN STOLEN FROM AMYNTOR (FATHER OF PHOENIX) BY AUTOLYCUS (ODYSSEUS' GRANDFATHER); AUTOLYCUS HAD PASSED IT ON TO AMPHIDAMUS, WHO PASSED IT ON TO MOLUS, WHO IN TURN PASSED IT ON TO HIS SON MERIONES. WHEN MERIONES LENT IT TO ODYSSEUS, IT HAD COME FULL CIRCLE, SO ODYSSEUS MIGHT WELL HAVE REGARDED IT AS A GOOD OMEN.

There was no rush of volunteers until Diomedes spoke up. It was a mission after his own heart, but he would feel more confident if he had a companion. Of course, once Diomedes had offered to go, everybody wanted to go with him; both the Ajaxes, Menelaus, Meriones, Nestor's son Thrasymedes, and Odysseus, who was always ready for a covert operation. Agamemnon was suddenly afraid for his brother, and intervened, telling Diomedes to choose any companion he liked, but not to feel that he should choose someone of high rank just for the sake of protocol:

Tydides Diomed, my heart's delight!
Choose thou thy comrade, whomso thou preferr'st;
Since many proffer, choose thou out the best:
Nor, through some over-reverence, pass thou by
The better man, nor take to thee the worse,
For majesty, or for respect of birth,
Albeit he be of some more royal race.

But Diomedes had already chosen. Odysseus. How could he choose any other—a brave-hearted and resourceful fighter, quick and vicious in a tight corner and loved by Athena—the man most likely to go on a dangerous mission behind enemy lines and make it back in one piece. Odysseus gruffly cut short Diomedes' praises; they should just get going—the stars were fading and two watches had gone past. Both men armed up, Diomedes took a sword, shield, and helmet, and Odysseus a bow and quiver. Meriones lent Odysseus his own precious helmet set with boars' teeth that his father had given him. As they left the rest of the group, Athena sent a sign. It was a heron—they could not see it but they heard it whoop. This lifted their hearts, and they prayed to Athena, promising rich sacrifice if she granted them success. Then the two fearsome warriors loped off into the night, like twin lions stalking through the blood and bodies toward the Trojan lines.

Hector's spy

Few had slept in the Trojan camp either. Hector had forbidden it. He also had called a council of war and he had a plan of his own. He asked for a volunteer, someone willing to slip through the Greek lines, sneak down to their ships, and find out how well guarded they were, and whether the Greeks were planning to leave or not.

Knowing his audience, he offered a handsome reward: a chariot and pair of horses, the best that could be looted from the Greeks.

There was a very long silence. Finally a volunteer spoke up. Unfortunately for Hector, this was no Diomedes or Odysseus, but a weasely creature called Dolon. He would do it, if Hector would swear on his scepter that Dolon would get the chariot and pair belonging to Achilles:

> But raise aloft thy sceptre; swear thereon
> To give me the enamell'd car and steeds
> Which bear the great Peleion* on the field.
> So I to thee will prove no idle spy.
> Nor disappoint thy hopes, but pierce their camp
> To Agamemnon's galley, where perchance
> They hold their council, or to flight or war.
>
> *Peleion = Achilles

Desperate for the spy to get moving, Hector swore this ludicrous oath on his scepter, knowing it was a false promise. But it was good enough for Dolon, who leaped up, slung on his bow, and put on his wolfskin cloak and a ferret-skin cap and set off eagerly.

Dolon was never to come back. He moved swiftly, but he was not quick enough for sharp-eyed Odysseus who spotted him out on the plain and nudged Diomedes. The very straggler they were seeking. They whispered together, planning to let the wretch get ahead of them and then rush him from behind, driving him toward the Greek lines. They crouched down in the dark among the corpses, waiting for him to pass.

The witless Dolon ran on. Suddenly he heard footsteps behind him; he stopped and turned, breathing hard, regretting his rash offer already. He tried to convince himself that it was a pair of fellow Trojans, come to tell him the mission had been aborted. Then he saw that they were Greeks. Off he sprang, running for dear life, but they ran him down like hounds coursing a hare. Dolon had almost reached the Greek lines when Diomedes shouted at him to stop and flung his spear, aiming ahead of his quarry, so that it skimmed over his shoulder and stuck into the ground in front of him. Dolon stopped dead in his tracks, and stood white-faced and gibbering with fear. Odysseus and Diomedes grabbed an arm each, and the wretch burst into tears. He begged for his life, offering a huge ransom; his father was rich and would pay anything as long as his son was kept alive.

Odysseus spoke amiably. Dolon should not worry himself—death should be the last thing on his mind; all he had to do was tell them what he was up to. Why was he

DOLON

DOLON THE SPY WAS A FECKLESS TROJAN YOUTH, DESCRIBED AS FAST ON HIS FEET BUT UGLY (WHEN MOST WARRIORS ARE DESCRIBED AS GODLIKE). HE WAS THE SON OF A RICH MAN, THE LONE BOY IN A FAMILY OF FIVE SISTERS, AND ONLY TOOK ON THE SPY MISSION BECAUSE HE BELIEVED HECTOR WOULD REWARD HIM RICHLY. HE ALSO BELIEVED THAT HIS FATHER'S RICHES WOULD RANSOM HIM, AND PROMISED BRASS, GOLD, AND WROUGHT IRON IF ODYSSEUS AND DIOMEDES WOULD LET HIM GO. TROY WAS A VERY RICH CITY, AND IT WAS NOT UNUSUAL FOR YOUNG MEN TO BE CAPTURED PRECISELY BECAUSE THEIR FATHERS WOULD PAY HANDSOMELY FOR THEIR RELEASE.

prowling about alone after dark? Out for some lucrative corpse-robbing? Sent by Hector to spy on the Greek fleet? Or was it just a bit of boyish bravado?

> *Take heart; nor let thy death be in thy thought.*
> *Rather speak freely all, and tell me this—*
> *Whither through night's dim darkness mak'st thou way*
> *Towards our fleet, whilst others are at rest?*
> *To strip some body? Or hath Hector sent*
> *To spy what now is passing in our ships?*
> *Or doth thine own brave heart thus prompt thee forth?*

Dolon's knees turned to jelly as he squeaked and stuttered and blamed everything on Hector who had misled him, bedazzling him with a prize of Achilles' very own chariot and horses. Finally he confessed that he was a spy.

Odysseus gave a long, slow grin. Now wasn't Dolon the superhero, risking all for Achilles' chariot and team of horses, particularly as he wouldn't be able to drive them—it was hard enough for Achilles, let alone a worm like Dolon. It was time to answer some questions. Where was Hector? Where was his armor? And his chariot? Where and how were the Trojan guard posted? What was their next plan? Were they going to stay where they were or withdraw to the city?

Dolon spilled every bean he had. He told them everything, fear making his voice tremble. Hector was in council; no guard had been posted because everyone in the Trojan camp was awake:

> *Hector, with all who have in senate seat,*
> *Holds council, clear of all the din, and near*
> *To Ilus'* tomb; but of the guards, great chief,*
> *Thou askest—they are on no fixèd posts*
> *To watch or save the camp; but, where the fires*
> *Amongst the Trojans (who needs must keep guard)*
> *Show blazing, there men wake, and each bids each*
> *Keep heedful watch ...*

Dolon ended with a graceless whine about how the so-called allies who had come to help Troy were all asleep—it was all right for them, they had no wives or family in Troy. Odysseus pressed on. Where were these allies camped? And Dolon told him exactly where all the allies were—but suddenly thought that he might save his skin with a bit

ILUS

ILUS, SON OF TROS AND CALLIRHOE, A DAUGHTER OF THE XANTHUS RIVER, WAS THE FOUNDER OF TROY, KNOWN AS ILIUM. WHEN HE ESTABLISHED THE CITY, HE ASKED ZEUS TO SEND A SIGN THAT HE HAD DONE THE RIGHT THING, AND THE GOD SENT THE PALLADIUM, A WOODEN IMAGE OF ATHENA. IT WAS BELIEVED THAT AS LONG AS THE PALLADIUM WAS SAFE IN THE TEMPLE BUILT FOR IT, ILIUM COULD NOT FALL. ILUS WAS THE FATHER OF LAOMEDON AND GRANDFATHER OF PRIAM.

of bribery. If Odysseus and Diomedes wanted some serious plunder, he recommended the newly arrived Thracian contingent who were in a vulnerable position:

> *Here lie the Thracians, on the skirts of all*
> *Alone, and late-arrived; and with them came*
> *Rhesus, the son of Eioneus, their King.*
> *Largest, most beauteous on this earth, his steeds,*
> *Whiter than snow, and footed like the winds,*
> *I late beheld; and eke his car is wrought*
> *In gold and silver; and of gold his arms,*
> *Of size prodigious, marvel to behold,*
> *Such as 'twould seem no mortal man might bear,*
> *But worthy to enclothe immortal Gods.*

The luckless Dolon implored the Greek pair either to take him to the ships, or just to tie him up and leave him where he was—they could go and see for themselves that he was telling the truth. But now that the crafty Odysseus had extracted all the information they needed, it was Diomedes' turn to play. Dolon was doomed, he said shortly. If they set him free, he'd be back tomorrow to spy or fight—he would have to be killed. Dolon begged Diomedes to spare his life, but Diomedes had no time for beggars. He lopped off Dolon's head with one quick stroke; his tongue was still wagging as his head bounced and rolled in the dust. Diomedes and Odysseus then tore off Dolon's armor, cap, and cloak, and held them aloft, shouting to Athena, the goddess of plunder. They stowed the loot in a tamarisk bush, marking it so they would recognize it on the way back, and prayed again to the goddess to guide them safely to the Thracian camp.

Thracian massacre

Odysseus and Diomedes moved swiftly on, stepping over corpses, discarded armor, and blood-filled furrows. Suddenly they stumbled on the Thracian outpost. Men lay fast asleep, their weapons set out beside them in neat rows, alongside their horses. In the middle lay Rhesus, their king; and beside him stood two magnificent white horses, tethered to the rail of a golden chariot. Recognizing him from Dolon's description, Odysseus urged Diomedes on:

THRACE

A COUNTRY ON THE MAINLAND NORTH OF THE HELLESPONT, IN AN AREA NOW SHARED BETWEEN GREECE, BULGARIA AND TURKEY. IT WAS THE HOME OF THE THRACIANS, STRONG ALLIES OF THE TROJANS.

This, Diomed, the man, and these the steeds,
Whereof, or e'er we slew him, Dolon told.
Now warm we to the work; 'tis not thy part
To stand full-arm'd and idle: loose the steeds;
Or ply thy sword, and be the steeds my care.

Ablaze with Athena's fury, Diomedes fell on the Thracians like a lion on a flock of sheep, laying about him with his sword, hewing at men as they lurched from sleep. He slaughtered twelve of the Thracians; the camp was sodden with their blood. Rhesus was killed last, still deep in sleep, but breathing heavily, oppressed by nightmares. As Diomedes hacked, Odysseus dragged the bodies out of the way; he wanted to have a clear run for the beautiful horses, which would be frightened by corpses and the stench of fresh blood. He uncoupled them from the chariot, and tied their reins together. Then he leaped onto one and lashed it with his bow and got the pair out of the carnage. He whistled urgently to Diomedes, who stood in the midst of the slaughter wondering what to do. Should he take the gleaming chariot and the gorgeous armor as plunder? Or should he stay a little longer and slay a few more Thracians? But the goddess Athena came to Diomedes and urged him fiercely to get back to the ships, before some other god noticed and came to the Trojans' aid. Wasting no more time, Diomedes leaped onto the other horse, and he and Odysseus galloped for the safety of the ships.

Athena was not wrong. On Olympus, Apollo was on the watch; he saw Athena helping Diomedes and Odysseus. Enraged he rushed down to the Thracian fighters, and woke up Hippocoon, a kinsman of Rhesus. Starting up with a jolt, Hippocoon wept to see the slaughtered men and Rhesus dead; his loud wailing brought other Trojans flocking to the site, to stare dumbly at the havoc wrought by the marauders.

Back at the ships

Pausing only to collect their plunder from the tamarisk bush, Odysseus and Diomedes charged back to the ships. Nestor heard them coming; he feared an attack and declared woefully that the Greeks had sent two of their best fighters off to their doom; but as he concluded his pessimistic outburst, Odysseus and Diomedes arrived, flushed with success. Comrades crowded round to embrace them, and Nestor asked the question on everybody's lips:

How got ye, tell me quick, these noble steeds?
Or by a foray on the camp of Troy?
Or did some God accost you and bestow
These miracles of radiance—like the sun?

Nestor had never seen such beautiful beasts, with their coats of burnished silver, and he had, as everyone knew, been around a bit. Surely a great god had given them?

Odysseus laughed and slapped Nestor on the back; of course they weren't a gift from the gods, the gods could do much better than that. These were the loot from a Thracian king whom Diomedes had slain, along with twelve others, and a worthless spy they had picked up; all in all, a good night's work.

Swaggeringly pleased with themselves and their success, with the cheers of their comrades ringing in their ears, Odysseus and Diomedes rode back to Diomedes' tent, where they tethered, fed, and watered the horses. Odysseus stowed the plunder on his galley, dedicating it to Athena. Then the two heroes walked into the sea to scour off the sweat and grime of battle. After a bath and a rub down with olive oil, they were ready for a meal, but not before they had poured libations to Athena, the goddess who had protected them.

Diomedes fell

on the

Thracians like

a lion on a

flock of sheep.

Book 11
AGAMEMNON IN GLORY

Agamemnon to the fore

INSTANT *ILIAD*

DAWN BREAKS ON THE
BATTLEFIELD FOR THE
THIRD DAY OF
FIGHTING, AND ZEUS
SENDS DOWN ERIS, THE
GODDESS OF STRIFE,
TO THE GREEK SHIPS,
INSPIRING THEM TO
ATTACK. BUT WHEN
AGAMEMNON IS
WOUNDED THE
GREEKS BEGIN TO FALL
BACK, UNTIL FINALLY
PATROCLUS DECIDES
THAT IT IS TIME TO
APPEAL TO HIS LORD
ACHILLES FOR HELP.

The terrible goddess Strife, dispatched by Zeus to the Greek fleet and carrying the symbol of battle, stood on Odysseus' ship at the center of the line and shrieked out an awful war cry, filling the hearts of the Greeks with the lust for killing:

> Thence loud and dread her shout the Goddess raised,
> In every Achaian kindling dauntless heart
> Strong to unending onset and affray;
> Yea, so that sudden sweeter seem'd the thought
> Of battle than aboard their hollow barks
> Home to their dear fatherland return!

Agamemnon enthusiastically pulled on his fine armor and took his sword, and shouted orders to his troops to prepare for battle. The warriors had their chariots drawn up along the outside of the Greek defensive ditch while they hurried forward. At the same time, the Trojans were assembling in battle order up on the high ground of the plain around Hector, whose bronze armor glinted in the early light. Then both sides leaped forward into attack, hacking swathes through their opponents like a harvester through a field of barley. The battle was witnessed with delight by Strife, but the other gods in Olympus were locked in dispute with Zeus because he was bringing glory to the Trojans.

The two sides fought through the morning, neither side giving ground, until toward noon the Greeks suddenly burst through the Trojan lines. Charging in through the gap, Agamemnon struck to right and left, killing any Trojan who opposed him, including two sons of Priam, Isus and Antiphus, in the same chariot. Then he glimpsed

Agamemnon, the overall
commander of the army of
Greek allies, led his men into
battle, intent on winning back
Sparta's honor for his brother
Menelaus and all those who
swore to protect Helen, his
abducted queen.

another chariot careering out of control. In it were cowering two brothers, Pisander and Hippolochus, the sons of the Trojan Antimachus, who had once argued in the Trojan assembly in favor of killing the two Greek ambassadors, Odysseus and Menelaus. Agamemnon fell upon them like a lion and the brothers soon begged him for mercy, offering him a great ransom to spare their lives. But Agamemnon was in no mood for reconciliation and was determined that they should pay for their father's treacherous behavior. He speared Pisander in the chest, and when Hippolochus leaped down to defend his brother's corpse, Agamemnon lopped off his arms and head and left the trunk of his body rolling like a log across the battlefield:

> As when upon an unhewn forest falls
> A fire consuming, and all sides the wind
> Rolls it together, root and branch the woods
> Sink prone before the onset of the flame;
> So 'fore the step of Agamemnon sank
> The crests of fleeing Trojans ...

Zeus continued to protect Hector from the flying missiles and the blinding dust, but all the time Agamemnon, his hands covered with blood and gore, was leading the Greek onslaught and pushing the Trojans back toward the gates of the city. Agamemnon had almost reached the Scaean Gate to the city when Zeus took up position on Mount Ida, armed with a thunderbolt, and sent his messenger Iris down to Hector in the middle of the battle. Iris told Hector that as long as he could see Agamemnon advancing, he was to keep fighting, but give ground. But the moment that Agamemnon was hit and took to his chariot, Zeus would give Hector the power to kill and carry on killing, all the way to the beached Greek ships.

Hector heard this message and took notice of it. He set off among the Trojans to rouse them to continue the fight. It was a grim battle, and at the gates, the Trojans turned and resisted. The Greeks in turn reinforced their push, with Agamemnon fighting in the front. The first Trojan to challenge him was the tall and handsome figure of Iphidamas. Agamemnon flung his spear at him as he approached but missed, and Iphidamas took the opportunity to stab Agamemnon in the midriff beneath his body armor. But the spear hit Agamemnon's silver belt and the point bent against it. Agamemnon pulled the spear shaft toward him and dealt Iphidamas a fatal blow in return. Agamemnon began to strip the body of its armor, but while he was intent on this, his attacker's grief-stricken brother Coön surprised him and pierced Agamemnon through the forearm with his spear.

Enraged, Agamemnon stabbed at Coön with his own spear as they struggled over Iphidamas' dead body, and made a fatal thrust. He cut off Coön's head, but Coön had managed to strike a vital blow. As long as the blood kept flowing, Agamemnon continued to wreak havoc in the Trojan lines, but when his wound started to dry out, he began to feel the pain. Finally, in great agony, Agamemnon leaped into his chariot and began to make his way back to the ships, urging the army around him to keep fighting:

> *"Friends, chiefs, and captains of Achaia's host!*
> *Remains for you to guard from off our sails*
> *The baleful battle; for to me great Zeus*
> *Grants not to fight the whole day out with Troy."*
> *He spoke, his driver tow'rd the hollow ships*
> *Thong'd the sleek horses, nothing loth they flew,*
> *Whose chests with foam, whose flanks with dust, grew white,*
> *As from the fray they bore the wounded King.*

Hector seizes the moment

Hector saw what had happened and realized that this was his chance. He rallied his troops, declaring that the best Greek fighter had left the field and Zeus had given him the victory. Hector ordered his men to drive their horses straight at the Greeks, and with that he dashed to the front line. Hector fell upon the leaders of the Greek army like a mighty storm, forcing them back toward the ships. Soon their retreat had turned into headlong flight.

Odysseus grabbed Diomedes and urged him to make a stand with him, saying that it would never be forgotten if they let Hector capture the ships. Diomedes agreed readily, though he did not think it would help them for long. It looked to him as though Zeus had decided that the Trojans should win. Nonetheless the two mighty warriors managed to halt the Trojan advance and gain some respite for the Greeks.

As the battle began to become confused, Hector saw that Odysseus and Diomedes had rallied the Greek troops and threw himself at them with a mighty shout, and with the Trojan battalions following close behind him. Diomedes flung his spear at Hector's head, and it glanced off the helmet which Apollo had given him without penetrating the metal. But the blow dazed Hector for a moment, and he sank to his

SCAEAN GATE

THE SCAEAN GATE, THE SCENE OF SO MUCH FIGHTING, WAS THE CEREMONIAL GATE IN THE NORTHWEST OF THE CITY WALLS OF TROY—BY THE CITADEL—AND BY TRADITION NEAR THE ONLY VULNERABLE PART OF THE WALL, BECAUSE, UNLIKE THE REST, IT HAD BEEN BUILT BY A MORTAL AND WAS MADE TOO THIN. THE LEGEND HAS IT THAT THE SCAEAN GATE, THROUGH WHICH HECTOR AND PARIS PASSED ON THEIR WAY OUT TO THE FIGHTING, WAS ONLY OPENED WHEN THE CITY WAS AT WAR.

MEDICINE

MACHAON WAS THE
SURGEON AND HEALER
FOR THE GREEK ARMY,
TOGETHER WITH HIS
BROTHER PODALEIRIUS,
AND AS SUCH HE WAS
ALSO A FORERUNNER
OF ANCIENT GREEK
MEDICINE. HE WAS THE
SON OF THE GOD
ASCLEPIUS, WHOSE
TEMPLES—WHERE
PATIENTS WERE GIVEN
HERBS TO HELP THEM
SLEEP AND DREAM—
BECAME THE FIRST
HOSPITALS. HEALTH
FOR THE ANCIENT
WORLD MEANT USING
HERBS TO HELP
BALANCE THE
"HUMORS" OR
EMOTIONS IN THE
BODY, AND MACHAON
USES HERBS AND
HERBAL OINTMENTS
TO HEAL THE
WOUNDED BODIES
OF HIS COMRADES.

knees. Diomedes struggled toward him through the fighting, eager to finish the Trojan hero off, but Hector recovered himself and managed to retreat in his chariot. Diomedes yelled angrily after him:

Cur! Who again hast 'scaped thy death this while!
Ill press'd thee hard: but Phoebus now once more
Hath saved thee, unto whom thou needs must make
Prayers endless ere thou venturest to the war.
Yet, let some god do battle on my side,
Next when we meet I ween I end thee quite;
Till then I turn me 'gainst whome'er I may.

Diomedes returned to the fray and began to strip the armor from one of his victims. Paris spotted him and took careful aim with his bow. He loosed an arrow that flew at Diomedes and pierced his right foot, going straight through and pinning Diomedes to the earth. Paris shouted in triumph, crowing that he wished he had killed Diomedes outright and released the Trojans from their terror of him.

Diomedes was not frightened by Paris, and though wounded, jeered scornfully at him for boasting about scratching his foot when he knew full well that he would not last long in a hand-to-hand fight:

Dumb falls the weapon from a dastard's arm;
But from my hand much otherwise the spear
Speeds, and, albeit it barely reach the foe,
Lifeless it makes him, and his children makes
Orphans—whose wife shall rend her cheeks for grief,
Whilst he lies rotting, reddening with his blood
The earth about; and round him, in good sooth,
More birds of prey than loving women crowd!

Odysseus dashed to Diomedes and watched while he heaved the arrow out of his foot. In great pain, Diomedes limped to his chariot and set off back toward the ships. All alone, Odysseus weighed up his options—to be accused of cowardice by retreating in the face of the enemy, or to be killed where he stood? Which should he do? Soon Odysseus was surrounded by eager young Trojans who set upon him like dogs on a wild boar. Odysseus struck down two of them but another succeeded in piercing his shield with a spear and wounding him in the ribs. Odysseus responded by roaring a threat at his assailant, who turned and fled, but to no avail: Odysseus thrust a spear between his shoulder blades. Odysseus' wound was not dangerous but when he pulled the spear from his side, blood poured out, giving encouragement to the Trojans. This decided Odysseus what to do and he gave ground, shouting for help as loudly as he could. Menelaus heard him and urged Great Ajax to come to help rescue him. When Ajax appeared, the Trojans scattered, and Menelaus took Odysseus' arm and led him back through the crowd.

While Ajax was cutting down the Trojan ranks before him, Hector had withdrawn to the banks of the Xanthus River, on the left of the battlefield. He was supported by his brother Paris, who stopped Machaon, one of the most effective Greek warriors, in his tracks with a three-barbed arrow that struck him in the right shoulder. At the urging of his colleagues, who knew the importance of a skilled healer like Machaon, Nestor loaded Machaon onto his chariot and raced him back to the ships. Then one of Hector's lieutenants alerted him to

Every warrior carried a shield, usually decorated with an image appropriate to him. Most shields were made of many layers of thick ox-hide glued together, sometimes reinforced with a layer of metal or wood. The shield crafted for Achilles by Hephaestus was made entirely of metal.

the furious assault of Ajax elsewhere on the battlefield, and so he galloped away from the fringes of the battle toward the Greek hero. Blood from the corpses on the ground splashed up from the hooves of his dashing horses and the wheels of his chariot, and when he tore into the Greeks they fell back. Even the mighty Ajax began to withdraw:

> *Till Father Zeus from throne on high awoke*
> *Spirit of fear in Ajax: first he stood*
> *Astonied, and behind him flung the shield;*
> *And timorously about him o'er the throng*
> *Looking, like some wild beast, hesitating*
> *He turn'd, yet oft wheel'd back, withdrawing slow*
> *One knee behind the other.*

Unwillingly, Ajax began to make his way back toward the ships. Occasionally he would turn on his pursuers, then once more he would retreat, the arrows and spears of the Trojans bouncing off his enormous shield. His friend Eurypylus saw what was happening and dashed forward to support him, striking out at the advancing Trojans. Paris saw him and drew his bow and fired, striking Eurypylus in the thigh. Brave Eurypylus then had to limp out of the front line, and as he staggered away he urged his colleagues to rally round Ajax.

The situation was hopeless, with most of the Greek leaders wounded or dead.

Patroclus takes an interest

At length, Nestor's chariot arrived back at the fleet with the wounded Machaon, watched from the stern of his own ship by Achilles. He called out for his companion Patroclus, who came to see why he was wanted. This obedience was to seal Patroclus' fate. Achilles said it looked as though the moment had arrived when the Greeks would come on their knees to beg him for help. He ordered Patroclus to see if it was Machaon who had been brought in wounded, because Achilles had not been able to see his face.

Patroclus set off to find out, and arrived at Nestor's just as they were treating Machaon's wound with a healing potion. Patroclus explained that Achilles had sent him and he must get back and report promptly, because as they all knew, his captain was not a patient man. Nestor responded angrily, asking why Achilles was so concerned about one warrior among so many. The old man recited a litany of the Greek losses:

> By shaft or sword the noblest all lie smit:
> A dart hath maim'd the might of Tydeus' Son;
> Odysseus, Agamemnon, wounded lie;
> Eurypylus hath arrow through the hip;
> And yet one more, this hero, from the war
> Pierced with an arrow, latest I have brought:
> And, though with power to save, Achilles sits
> Unpitying still!

Agamemnon and Menelaus were related to Zeus by marriage, and so might legitimately expect more support from him. Zeus and Leda were the parents of Helen, wife to Menelaus. Clytemnestra, Helen's sister, was the wife of Agamemnon, brother of Menelaus. Electra was one of their daughters.

ELECTRA   LEDA   AGAMEMNON   ZEUS

Nestor again bewailed the fact that he was no longer the youthful warrior that he had been. Then he reminded Patroclus what his father had told him before they left for the siege—to remember that although he was not as noble or strong as Achilles, he was the elder of the two and he should give him a lead. Nestor urged Patroclus to try to persuade Achilles into rejoining the fight. At the very least, Achilles might allow Patroclus and the Myrmidons to give the Greeks some support. Nestor then suggested a cunning strategem to Patroclus:

And let him clothe thee in his own bright mail:
That so the Trojans shall behold in thee
His image, and withdraw them back awhile,
And so th' Achaians gain some breathing-space—
Short though it be, some respite from the war.
They are all spent, and ye unworn and fresh;
Your very battle-cry shall drive their host
Back routed from our galleys to their town.

Nestor's words moved Patroclus and he set off back to Achilles at a run. As he passed Odysseus' ship, Patroclus met Eurypylus, the sweat pouring from his brow and the blood still gushing from the wound in his thigh. Patroclus was aghast and asked if the battle was lost. Eurypylus replied that the situation was hopeless, with most of the Greek leaders wounded or dead. He asked Patroclus to take him back to his ship, since the healers were injured or in the thick of the fighting. Patroclus remembered his mission to Achilles, but nonetheless he helped the limping Eurypylus, and laid him on the floor to tend to his wound.

THE MYRMIDONS

THE ELITE TROOPS UNDER THE LEADERSHIP OF ACHILLES WHO CAME, LIKE HIM, FROM THESSALY IN GREECE, AND—AGAIN LIKE ACHILLES—BEGAN THE *ILIAD* SITTING OUT THE FIGHTING IN SUPPORT OF THEIR SULKING CHIEF. THEIR BRAVERY AND SKILL IN BATTLE MADE THE MYRMIDONS FEARSOME OPPONENTS. IT WAS SAID THAT THEIR RACE WAS TURNED FROM ANTS INTO MEN BY ZEUS TO KEEP ACHILLES' UNCLE, TELAMON, COMPANY. THEY WERE ALSO BELIEVED TO BE THE FIRST RACE TO BUILD SHIPS WITH SAILS.

MENELAUS · HELEN · CLYTEMNESTRA

Book 12
HECTOR REACHES THE WALL

The Trojans advance

The wooden defenses in front of the Greek fleet echoed with the sound of Trojan missiles, with Hector roaring his troops on to victory like an enraged lion:

> *... But now the cry*
> *Of battle ran along its strong-built heights*
> *Flamelike, and smitten rang its beamy towers.*
> *Gradual the Argives by the scourge of Zeus*
> *Straiten'd against their galleys 'gan retire*
> *Subdued; for Hector breathed a fear upon them,*
> *And, as his wont, fought with a whirlwind's force.*

The Greeks were now trapped between their own wall and the fighting prowess of Hector, inspired as he was by Zeus. It was time to unleash the Trojan forces against the wooden walls. But although Hector marched up and down the Trojan lines urging them on, none of the chariots—not even his own horses—dared to leap the moat. Time after time, the horses stopped at the brink of the ditch, whinnying furiously.

It certainly was a challenge. The lip of the ditch overhung the edge all the way along, and the approach was defended with a row of sharpened stakes. On the other side there was only a narrow space before the wall, giving the charioteers nowhere to dismount and fight. But though the horses dared not cross, the foot soldiers were willing to try, and the Trojan warrior Polydamas was soon urging this policy on Hector. He pointed out that it was almost impossible to cross the ditch by chariot, and even if a few of the Trojans managed to get to the other side, they would be wiped out by the Greeks:

Hear therefore, and obey as I advise;
Let our men hold our chariots on the brink
Whilst we in arms complete and close array
Move, side by side, round Hector; nor the foe
Will stand against us, if their hour be come.

Hector agreed to Polydamas' plan, and soon the other Trojan charioteers were leaping down from their chariots, fully armed and organizing themselves into five contingents. The biggest contingent was commanded by Hector and Polydamas. Together the Trojan warriors drew themselves up in close formation, with their shields touching along the line, confident that nothing would prevent them from storming the ships.

Only one Trojan leader, Asius, refused to abandon either his chariot or his charioteer and advanced with his contingent over a crossing used by the retreating Greeks. He found that the gates in the wall were still open, to allow the retreating Greek forces to enter. Convinced that victory was in his grasp, Asius and his men rushed toward the gates, yelling their battle cries. But they were met by two Greek champions from the warlike Lapith race, Polypoetes and Leonteus, who had dashed out from inside the ramparts when they saw the advancing Trojans. Like wild boars facing a mob of huntsmen and hounds, they lashed out this way and that, supported by the men on the wall above them, who hurled stones down at the attackers. The helmets and armor rang as the rocks crashed against them. So savagely did the Lapiths fight that the Trojans were halted, and the exasperated Asius swore at Zeus for allowing the Greeks to hold on so tenaciously. But Zeus favored Hector, and was not about to let Asius take the glory.

As the Trojan contingents reached other gates in the wall, a series of fires broke out as the Greeks defended their ships. All the gods on the Greek side who were looking down from Olympus were in despair, but the odds seemed to be shifting a little more in their favor. The two Lapiths carried on their mighty offensive, killing many of those who had rashly followed Asius' chariot, and stripping their armor.

> *Together the Trojan warriors drew themselves up in close formation.*

A bad omen

CHARIOTS

WAR IN THE *ILIAD* WAS AN ARISTOCRATIC PURSUIT. THERE WERE FOOT-SOLDIERS ON BOTH SIDES, BUT THE FEARSOME WEAPONS WERE WIELDED BY THE WEALTHY WARRIORS, DRIVEN AROUND THE BATTLEFIELD IN THEIR FOUR-HORSE CHARIOTS—RATHER LIKE TAXIS, THAT DROPPED THEM OFF FOR COMBAT WITH THEIR OPPONENTS. THE MAJORITY OF THE ARMY MAY EVEN HAVE BEEN MADE UP OF THESE WARRIORS AND THEIR CHARIOTEERS, AND IT WAS THEY AND THEIR CAVALRY WHO WERE THE DECISIVE FACTOR IN BATTLE.

The Trojans under Polydamas and Hector were still waiting by the ditch wondering what to do. They had seen an eagle flying from the left across the front of the army, with a blood-red snake in its talons—a clear omen of bad luck. The snake was still twisting in the air and bit the eagle in the neck, forcing it to release its hold. The horrified Trojans watched the snake writhing on the ground in the middle of them. Seeing this, Polydamus risked contradicting his commander and advised Hector not to advance toward the ships. Since the eagle had failed to get home to its nest with its catch, this clearly meant that, even if the Trojans managed to break through to the ships, they would be forced back in disarray.

Hector was furious and accused Polydamas of having lost his senses. He reminded him of Zeus' promise, and mocked the idea of taking notice of mere birds, whatever way they flew. The only omen that mattered to him was to fight for his country:

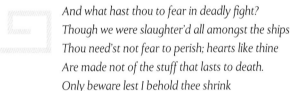

And what hast thou to fear in deadly fight?
Though we were slaughter'd all amongst the ships
Thou need'st not fear to perish; hearts like thine
Are made not of the stuff that lasts to death.
Only beware lest I behold thee shrink
Or others by that guiling tongue entice;
That moment shouldst thou perish by my spear.

With this, Hector led the charge and his own men followed him with ear-splitting yells. From the mountains, Zeus flung a hurricane after them that blew dust straight at the Greek ships, bewildering the defenders. Encouraged by this sign of favor from the gods, the Trojans redoubled their efforts to break through the wall, pulling at the battlements and trying to lever up the sunken buttresses that supported them. But every time they succeeded in creating a breach, the Greeks filled it with their oxhide shields and flung stones at the enemy as they gathered below.

All along the wall, the two Ajaxes were encouraging the defenders, and giving orders to those who had abandoned the fight. They forbade anyone to turn back to the ships. There was only one way out, and that was forward, with trust in Zeus that he would help the Greeks to fight off the attack. A hail of stones and rocks filled the air, thrown by the Trojans or flung back by the Greeks as the wall echoed with crashes along its entire length. The battle was furious, but neither side seemed to be giving way.

The might of Sarpedon

The Trojan ally Sarpedon, prince of Lycia, decided that bold action was required. Holding his huge round shield before him, and brandishing two spears, he sought out his fellow Lycian Glaucus, and urged him to justify the privileged reputation they enjoyed among the Lycians:

> *O mine own friend! If haply, by escape*
> *From this one field, thenceforward we might live*
> *Immortal and unaging, nor myself*
> *Would risk me thus, nor bid thee with me seek*
> *The glory that such onset brings a man.*
> *But, since ten thousand deadly dooms beset*
> *Our lives, and vain the hope to shun them all,*
> *Let us still onward, whether to bestow*
> *Renown on others or exalt our own!*

With these rousing words, Sarpedon and Glaucus together led the powerful Lycian contingent toward the ramparts.

The defender of that part of the wall, Menestheus, saw them coming with horror. He sent an urgent message to both Ajaxes warning them that death was staring them all in the face. Great Ajax followed the messenger back, together with his half-brother Teucer, the bowman. By the time they arrived, the Lycian leaders were already swarming over the battlements like a black cloud. Ajax reached the top of the wall and hit the first Lycian he saw over the head with a rock, smashing his helmet into four pieces and crushing his skull. The dead man plummeted from the ramparts like a diver. Teucer's arrow meanwhile struck Glaucus in the arm. Glaucus leaped down from the wall to make sure none of the Greeks could see that he was wounded.

Sarpedon was horrified, but there was no time to slacken. He stabbed at the nearest Greek with his spear, and used the shaft to drag the man over the wall, his armor clattering about him. Then he put his hands on the battlements and a whole length of brickwork came away, exposing a large breach for his comrades.

Ajax and Teucer, realizing where the greatest danger lay, both concentrated on Sarpedon himself. Zeus saved him from Teucer's arrow, which hit the gleaming shoulder strap across his chest, but Ajax's stab at his shield stopped his advance for a moment—long enough for him to call out to the Lycians following him:

SARPEDON

SARPEDON WAS A LYCIAN PRINCE AND IN ALLIANCE WITH THE TROJANS. BUT HE IS DIFFERENT, BECAUSE HE WAS ALSO A SON OF ZEUS BY A MORTAL MOTHER, LAODAMIA. AS SUCH, HE WAS UNDER THE GODS' PROTECTION, AND WHEN ZEUS RELUCTANTLY HAD TO LET EVENTS TAKE THEIR COURSE, RESULTING IN SARPEDON'S DEATH AT THE HANDS OF PATROCLUS, APOLLO CLEANED HIS BODY, COVERED IT WITH AMBROSIA, AND SWEPT IT AWAY TO LYCIA FOR AN HONORABLE BURIAL.

GREEK DEFENSES

WHENEVER THEY WERE
IN THE ASCENDANT,
THE TROJANS
THREATENED TO BURN
THE SHIPS, DRAWN UP
ON THE BEACH, WHICH
BROUGHT THE GREEKS
TO THEIR CITY. IF THEY
COULD, IT WOULD
SPELL COMPLETE
VICTORY: NOT EVEN
THE GREEK WOUNDED
WOULD BE ABLE TO
GET HOME. THAT WAS
WHY THE GREEKS BUILT
THEIR OWN WALLS
AND BATTLEMENTS IN
A GIANT CIRCLE
AROUND THE SHIPS,
WITH DEFENSIVE
GATES, AND—AROUND
THE OUTSIDE —A
DITCH TO PREVENT A
CHARGE BY CAVALRY
OR CHARIOTS FROM
OVERWHELMING THEM.
IT WAS THEIR OWN
CITY FACING TROY.

Ho, Lycians! Slack ye thus your olden might?
Hopeless for me, how strong soe'er I show,
Singly to burst a path onto their fleet:
On then, and help; in numbers lies our strength!

But although they swarmed up into the breach that their leader had made, the defending Greeks were also reinforced and the desperate battle that followed there gave no advantage to either side. Blood drenched the battlements the whole length, and from both sides.

Despite the slaughter, the battle was disintegrating into stalemate. Neither side could win the upper hand. The Trojans pushed forward with confidence, and yet the Greeks managed to hold the line and defend their walls. Then suddenly, Zeus gave Hector the long-promised advantage. He was the first to penetrate the Greek defenses, the first to get inside the Greek wall. Once there, he screamed back at all his men, urging the rest of the army to smash the defenses and to set fire to the ships:

Once more into the breach! Up, Troy, and burst
Their bulwark, and with fire consume their ships!

There was not a man in the Trojan army who failed to hear him. They charged at the wall and began to scale it with their spears in their hands. Hector then seized the most enormous rock: it was broad at one end and then sharpened to a point, and would take at least two men to lever it up from the ground if they were to try

it these days. Yet the rock was made especially light for Hector by Zeus, and he lifted it easily. Hardly feeling the weight at all, Hector stood in front of the main gates, legs braced to keep him steady. Then he flung the stone into the middle of the gate, putting his full weight behind the throw, and burst the doors off their pivots on both sides. The planks were smashed and the crossbars on the inside gave way. Hector leaped through, his face as black as night, brandishing a spear in each fist, his armor shining like a terrible fire in the evening light:

> *Both hinges sheer he broke; with ponderous fall*
> *The rock rush'd inward far, and loud the crack*
> *And crash of shatter'd panel, nor the bars*
> *Held in their sockets, and the timbers flew*
> *In fragments, rent and riven by the shock.*
> *Leap'd then the glorious hero through the breach,*
> *Like dreadful Night in aspect, but his form*
> *One blaze of fiery armour, and a spear*
> *In either hand: no might, save might of Gods,*
> *Could stay him: and his eyeballs flash'd with fire.*

Only a god could have stopped Hector at that moment, and he turned to his army behind him and urged them on after him across the wall. In a moment they were dashing over the Greek defenses—all that protected their ships—and some were even fighting their way straight through the gate. In a panic, the Greeks fled back toward their ships and the battle reached a new intensity of fury. There seemed to be no end to it.

Warriors on both sides showed a variety of fighting skills. Spears were the weapon of choice for distance fighting, and spearmen carried swords and axes as back-up to use when fighting in close combat. Archers usually fought light, wearing little armor, and staying out of spear range.

Book 13
POSEIDON RISES

The sea god intervenes

Just when the Trojans were pressing hard around the black, beached hulls, Zeus, seeing that he had fulfilled his promise to Thetis, turned his great mind away from the battlefield. It never occurred to him that any other god would dare interfere. But his brother Poseidon, the maker of earthquakes and god of the sea, was watching, perched on the highest peak of Samothrace. And when he saw the Greeks being overrun, Poseidon was consumed with rage at Zeus. He stormed down the mountain in four bounds, and dived down to his vast underwater palace. Hitching up his horses and strapping on his battle armor, he drove flat out across the sea toward the beached Greek ships. Waves parted joyfully for him, and Poseidon flew over them so fast that the great bronze axle under his chariot did not even get wet. He pulled up in a great underwater cave between the islands of Imbros and Tenedos, tethered his horses, and strode off through the sea toward the beleaguered Greek encampment.

As Poseidon rose from the waves, the Trojans were engulfing the Greeks, screaming their terrible battle cries, aflame with Hector's pride. They were intent on taking the ships. Disguising himself as the seer Calchas, the god immediately butttonholed the two Ajaxes, urging them to concentrate their efforts at the most vulnerable point, where Hector was battering at the Greek lines. Poseidon was sure that the combined strength and skill of the Ajaxes could crush Hector, even if he was Zeus-inspired:

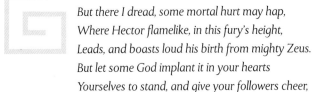

> But there I dread, some mortal hurt may hap,
> Where Hector flamelike, in this fury's height,
> Leads, and boasts loud his birth from mighty Zeus.
> But let some God implant it in your hearts
> Yourselves to stand, and give your followers cheer,

Poseidon, the god of the seas and waters of the world, crossed the seas in a golden chariot drawn by immortal white steeds, and so was also considered the god of horses. Achilles' stallions, Balius and Xanthus, were a wedding gift from Poseidon to Peleus, Achilles' father. Poseidon was a quarrelsome deity, often feuding with Hera, Athena, and Zeus.

Then, though the great Olympian fires him on,
Ye yet may stave his onset off the ships.

As Poseidon spoke, he struck them both with his staff, and they felt their hearts lighten and their spirits rise; as one, they ran toward the fighting. Little Ajax suspected they had been touched by a god, and both the warriors felt the power of Poseidon flow up from their hearts through their limbs to their weapons as they plunged into the fray.

Poseidon moved on, invisible among the ranks, yet stirring up the courage of warriors who were slack-limbed with weariness and filled with despair as they saw the Trojans overrunning them. They rallied round the two Ajaxes, forming into two tightly knit fighting units, shoulder to shoulder, shield to shield, so close that the crests on their helmets entwined. Their blood ran hot and their hearts were on fire, and they did not waver. The Trojan charge, with Hector in the lead, fell upon them like an avalanche. It seemed he would bowl straight through their ranks past the ships and into the sea, killing all the way. But the tidal wave of Trojan forces crashed against the solid shield wall, and broke up under the deadly bristling of Greek swords and spears. Hector reeled back, but only for a moment, instantly shouting to his men to regroup and stand firm—Zeus was with them:

Stand, Trojans, Lycians! Dardan men-at-arms,
Stand firm; the enemy will not stay me long,
Though they now gather, like some tower, four square;
But soon shall turn, if Zeus inspires me true,
The Thunderer, Herè's Lord, of Gods supreme.

The Ajaxes take on Hector

Deiphobus, son of Priam, strode out of the Trojan ranks, and charged at the Greeks. Meriones hurled his spear, skewering the center of the Trojan's shield, but the spear snapped off at the socket. Cursing, Meriones ran back to his lines for a replacement. Teucer the deadly archer brought down Imbrius, one of Priam's best allies, and Great Ajax was on him as he fell, thrusting a spear in behind his ear. Teucer darted forward, eager to seize his prize. Hector hurled his spear at him, but the nimble archer swerved and it hit Amphimachus, grandson of Poseidon, shearing open his chest. Now it was Hector's turn to rush for his battle plunder, but Great Ajax

Poseidon moved on, invisible among the ranks, yet stirring up the courage of the warriors.

lunged at him with a spear; it did not find its mark through Hector's armor, but it was powerful enough to drive him aside, giving the Greeks time to pull the dead out of the fray. Amphimachus was taken back to the Greek camp, but the two Ajaxes fell upon the Trojan Imbrius' body like lions worrying a dead goat; they lifted it high, stripping off the armor in midair. Little Ajax, in revenge for the death of Amphimachus, sliced the head from the body and sent it spinning across the battlefield, to land in the dust at Hector's feet.

Poseidon was beside himself; his own grandson Amphimachus had been mown down by the raging Hector. As the god went through the Greek camp, he came across the great charioteer, Idomeneus. Taking the form of Thoas, captain of the Aetolian contingent, the outraged Poseidon started right in on the Cretan. What had become of all those Greek threats to destroy the Trojans? All just big talk? If he was surprised at this outburst, Idomeneus did not show it; as far as he was concerned, the situation was no fault of any mortal warrior, but the workings of the unfathomable will of Zeus. He implored Thoas not to lose heart:

> *My fear is, peradventure it seems good*
> *To Kronos' Son supreme, that all the host*
> *Should perish far from Argos nameless here.*
> *But, Thoas—since of old thou ever lov'dst*
> *The battle, and to chide whom else soe'er*
> *Thou sawest slack—oh, change not from thy wont,*
> *Change not thyself, and cheer all others on.*

And Poseidon answered as Thoas, cursing all cowards as nothing but carrion for scavenging dogs. He and Idomeneus should arm up, and go to war shoulder to shoulder. Even cowards could make their mark if they banded together, so how much more effective might two skilled fighters like themselves be? And with that, Poseidon passed on through the ranks.

Fired up for the fight, Idomeneus reached his tent, strapped on his armor, snatched up two spears, and emerged bedazzling in his bronze war gear. He ran into Meriones, his second-in-command, who had returned to replace his spear. To save time, Idomeneus offered him one from his arsenal of plundered gear. The two strode grimly to war, gleaming and confident in their bright bronze, discussing tactics. The center was secure enough—Teucer and the two Ajaxes were giving it to Hector blow for blow, and Great Ajax would yield to no one, god or mortal. The Cretan captains decided to head for the left:

AMPHIMACHUS

POSEIDON'S GRANDSON, THE SON OF CTEATUS, WHO HAD ONCE FOUGHT OFF HERACLES, BUT WAS LATER KILLED BY HIM. AMPHIMACHUS HAD BEEN ONE OF HELEN'S SUITORS, AND SO LED THE EPEANS TO HELP RESCUE HER. HE WAS KILLED BY HECTOR, AROUSING POSEIDON'S GREAT WRATH.

IDOMENEUS

KING OF CRETE,
GRANDSON OF MINOS,
ALLY OF AGAMEMNON,
AND LEADER OF THE
CRETAN CONTINGENT
OF EIGHTY SHIPS. A
RENOWNED
CHARIOTEER,
IDOMENEUS FOUGHT
SUCCESSFULLY, DESPITE
BEING OLDER THAN
MOST OF THE GREEK
CAPTAINS. HE WAS
ONE OF THE
WARRIORS IN THE
TROJAN HORSE, AND
AFTER THE WAR,
SAILED HOME SAFELY
TO CRETE—ALTHOUGH
IN SOME ACCOUNTS,
TO ESCAPE FROM A
STORM HE HAD TO
PROMISE POSEIDON
THAT HE WOULD
SACRIFICE THE FIRST
THING HE SAW WHEN
HE GOT HOME—AND
SO HAD TO KILL HIS
OWN SON.

> To none of mortal race, to none who eat
> The fruits of earth, to none whom spear can pierce,
> Or sword can wound, or monstrous stone can crush,
> Will Telamonian Ajax yield in arms:
> Not ev'n before the great Destroyer of men
> Achilles need he yield in standing fight,
> Though none may vie with him for speed of foot.
> Then let us to the left, and learn, if there
> We conquer, or bestow, renown this day.

When the Trojans saw Idomeneus and Meriones blazing in their battle gear, they shouted and charged at them. Suddenly there was pitched battle, warriors caught up in the whirling fog of war, swords and spears clashing, flesh ripping, eyes blinded by terrible bright armor, chaos to terrify all but the most battle hardened.

And so, using men as their weapons, Zeus and Poseidon, the Olympian brothers warred against each other. Zeus strove openly for the Trojans. A short-term victory for Hector would make Achilles' eventual triumph even more glorious. Yet he did not want the Greeks destroyed—all he wanted was to keep his promise to Thetis and her strong-willed son. But Poseidon, intimidated by his older, more powerful brother, worked in secret to urge on the Greek forces, roaming the ranks disguised as an anonymous soldier. The gods pulled mercilessly on the great twisted rope of war, strangling both sides and cutting them off at the knees.

Idomeneus the killer

Idomeneus rampaged through the Trojans, spreading panic. He killed Othryoneus, who had come to Priam's aid out of love for his daughter Cassandra, thrusting his spear through shield and armor to pierce his bowels. As Idomeneus was dragging him off, his comrade Asius charged him down, but the Cretan was too fast for him, shafting him through the throat so that Asius fell from his chariot screaming in agony. His driver lacked the wit to stop, and he was run through by Antilochus, Nestor's son, who forked him out of the chariot like a hay bale.

Crying vengeance for Asius, Deiphobus hurled his spear at Idomeneus, who raised his great round shield just in time, so that the shaft screeched off its edge and struck

Hypsenor through the heart. Deiphobus jeered in triumph; Asius had not died unavenged. The Greeks wept, and Antilochus ran and hid Hypsenor's body with his shield, and helped drag the corpse away back to the ships.

Idomeneus raged on, intent on sending as many Trojans into eternal black night as he could, or to die trying. He stumbled on a royal prey, Alcathous, brother-in-law to Aeneas; feeling the power of Poseidon run through him, Idomeneus plunged his spear into Alcathous' heart, felling him on the spot. And as the Trojan sprawled on the ground, the spear quivering in its mark, Idomeneus taunted Deiphobus. Deiphobus stood in a dilemma—should he pull back to get help or rush the arrogant Cretan? Deciding that he needed support, he ran off to get Aeneas, whom he found idling at the very edge of the battlefield, away from the fighting. Aeneas was angry at Priam for treating him so meanly even though he was the most deserving of honor. Deiphobus burst in on this reverie of self-pity, urging Aeneas to come and help shield the body of his kinsman. His words stirred Aeneas' fighting spirit, and together they charged at Idomeneus. The Cretan held his ground, bristling like an old boar at bay; but because he had not become a hardened old warrior by indulging in futile gestures of pointless bravado, he shouted out for his comrades—Aphareus, Deipyrus, Ascalaphus, Meriones, and Antilochus—to come and help him:

> *Friends, hither haste, and help, where I now stand*
> *Alone against Aeneas; quick of foot*
> *Is he, and much I dread his near approach;*
> *For strong is he in fight to slay his man,*
> *And his the chiefest strength, the flower of youth.*
> *Yet, were our years, as are our hearts, the same,*
> *Singly betwixt us were the issue tried,*
> *Whether to his great glory or to mine.*

Idomeneus' comrades rushed to his aid, massing their shields around him, but many more answered Aeneas' cry for backup. Everyone closed in for the kill, contending around the body of Alcathous. Idomeneus and Aeneas scrambled to get a shot at each other. Aeneas threw first, but Idomeneus swerved, and the spear stuck harmless in the ground. Idomeneus threw his own spear, but missed the target, slicing the Trojan Oenamus through the belly instead. Idomeneus tore his blood-stained lance from the still-writhing body, but did not have the strength to strip the armor; the enemy hacked at him mercilessly, and he retreated under their blows, one desperate step at a time. Deiphobus tried his luck, hurling a second spear at Idomeneus, but he

POSEIDON

POSEIDON WAS THE BROTHER OF ZEUS, AND GOD OF ALL WATERS AND THE SEA AND THE ORIGINATOR OF EARTHQUAKES. DURING THE TROJAN WAR, HE WAS AN ARDENT SUPPORTER OF THE GREEKS, INTERVENING TO HELP THEM AGAINST ZEUS' WILL; POSEIDON LOATHED THE TROJANS BECAUSE HE HAD ONCE BEEN ENSLAVED TO KING LAOMEDON, AND HAD BUILT THE CITY WALLS FOR HIM, BUT LAOMEDON HAD RENEGED ON THE AGREED PAYMENT. POSEIDON ALWAYS GAVE WAY TO ZEUS, BUT RESENTED THIS VERY MUCH, BECAUSE HE FELT THAT HE WAS AN EQUAL, NOT A SUBORDINATE.

missed again and struck Ascalaphus instead. Now Ascalaphus was the son of Ares, the god of war; but the father heard nothing of his son's death agony, as he sat confined with the other gods in Olympus, pinned into inactivity by the sheer will of Zeus.

Deiphobus ripped the helmet from the head of Alcathous' corpse, but Meriones leaped on him, skewering his arm with his spear. Screaming, Deiphobus dropped the helmet, and Meriones tore the spear from his arm. Groaning and gushing blood, Deiphobus was dragged out of the fighting by his brother Polites. But for others, the fighting roared on. Aeneas slit the throat of Aphareus so thoroughly that his head fell sideways on his neck; Antilochus slashed Thoon across the back, severing his spine, sending him sprawling headlong—and as he crouched by the body, tearing off the fine armor, Poseidon protected him. Adamas, son of Asius, rammed his spear into Antilochus' shield, but Poseidon shattered it where it struck. Adamas tried to get away, but Meriones caught him, spearing him through the belly and he sank to the ground clasping the spear shaft, writhing and shuddering like a wild bull hobbled by men's ropes. Meriones put an end to his agony, wrenching the spear from his entrails and darkness came upon him. In revenge, the Trojan Helenus brought his huge sword down on Deipyrus' head, smashing off his helmet.

Menelaus came from nowhere, and charged toward Helenus, screaming his battle cry and brandishing his newly sharpened spear, just as Helenus was notching arrow on bow. Both let fly at once. Helenus' arrow hit Menelaus square in the chest, but bounced harmlessly off his armor. Menelaus had aimed his spear at the Trojan archer's hand, and it hit true, plunging straight through, pinning the hand to the polished bow. Helenus fell back, his bow arm now useless. Then Menelaus dispatched Pisander, thrusting a sword through his face so hard that the Trojan's eyeballs dropped out of his head and fell bloody into the dust. Pisander doubled up and crashed to the ground. Menelaus struck a triumphant pose, pressing a heel down on his dead foe's chest and bragging that all the Trojans would end up as corpses as wretched as this one if they did not leave the Greek ships alone. Did they not know when to call time, either on war or shamelessness? Did they not realize that it was only because Zeus was favoring them for a time that they had got anywhere near the Greek ships? Was there no limit to their blood lust?

Of all things else comes sweet satiety;
Of love, and slumber, and melodious song,
And dance delicious; things of more delight
And more to be desired than fierce affray;
Yet Troy will never have enough of war.

Menelaus stripped the dead Pisander of his arms and armor and threw them to his comrades to take back to the ships. As he turned to plunge back into the mêlée, he narrowly escaped the spearthrust of Harpalian, the Paphlagonian prince. It was Meriones, covering Menelaus' back, who brought the Trojan down with a fatal arrow.

Hector regroups

Meanwhile, Hector, battering the Greek line at the center, had heard nothing of how his men were being mauled by the Greeks, inspired by the power of the sea god. Hector hammered relentlessly at the point where he had broken through the defensive wall, aiming at the ships belonging to Ajax and Protesilaus. Wave after wave of Trojan cavalry pounded this weak spot; against them stood allied troops from Boeotia, Ionia, and Epea. They held Hector but could not drive him back, not even the handpicked Athenian elite led by Menestheus. The two Ajaxes fought side by side, backed up by a team of loyal comrades. The Locrians, who fought light, with no armor and only bows and slings for weapons, stood out of range from the main battle, raining a continuous and deadly shower of missiles onto the Trojan fighters.

It was beginning to look as if the Trojans might be pushed back to the city. Then Polydamas spoke bluntly to his leader, forcing him to look sensibly at their position. Just because Hector believed he was invincible, empowered by Zeus, did not mean all the other fighters were. Their military position was becoming untenable. They should withdraw, review tactics, and decide whether to press on, trusting to Zeus to make them victorious, or back off to the breaches, to regroup. There was still Achilles to contend with; he could join the fight at any time. Polydamas was for regrouping:

Therefore retire awhile, and hither call
The noblest chieftains, hence to take survey,
Whether to charge in onset midst their barks,
Should Heav'n vouchsafe to us such mastery,
Or to withdraw, if need be, still unharm'd.
Myself I dread, lest soon Achaia's host
Mete back with ample usury their debt
Of yester-eve; whose chiefest hero still
Abides unroused, unsated of affray—
Who will not always hold him thus aloof.

Hector listened, and ordered Polydamas to stay put, as a rallying point for the Trojan troops. Then he stormed along the lines, searching for his trusted captains—Deiphobus, Helenus, Othryoneus, Asius, and Adamas. He could not find them, but he did come across his brother Paris, urging on his troops, and angrily demanded to know where all his officers were:

> *Foul-omen'd Paris! fair in form alone!*
> *Infatuate, soft beguiler of fond girls!*
> *Where is Deiphobus? And where the might*
> *Of royal Helenus? And Asius' Son?*
> *And Asius, son of noble Hyrtacus?*
> *And where Othryoneus? Alas, this day*
> *Ilion* hath toppled headlong from her height,*
> *Yea, utter ruin now must surely come.*
>
> ** Ilion = Troy*

Paris replied stoutly that Hector was blaming him unjustly. He and his men had been holding their ground against great odds, never giving an inch. All Hector's brave captains were dead or wounded, no use in battle, Troy's great loss. Hector must lead them on now, and they would gladly follow him as long as their strength held out:

> *... Lead therefore thou,*
> *Whither thy heart and spirit prompt thee on;*
> *We will be near behind thee undismay'd,*
> *Nor blench, so far as in us lies the strength;*
> *For, howsoe'er the spirit burn to war,*
> *No man can pass the measure of his strength.*

These dauntless words helped make the bad news a little more bearable. Paris followed his brother back into the thick of the fighting, where Polydamas had gathered their allies. Among them were some welcome new faces, fresh troops from Ascania. The new Trojan front rolled like a boiling sea down on the Greeks, with Hector the crest of the wave. He surged along the Greek lines, charging them, taunting them, willing them to crack. It was Great Ajax who finally met his challenge, stepping out of the ranks to face him down contemptuously. Did Hector really think he was frightening them, when everyone knew that it was Zeus who was pulling the strings? He would never reach the ships. Troy would burn first:

All Hector's brave captains were dead or wounded, no use in battle.

Draw nearer, friend! why fright'st thou Argos' sons
Thus vainly? Though the evil scourge of Zeus
This day subdues us, not so all untrain'd
Are we, that merest show should fright us back.
Thy soul aspires, I ween, to burn our ships;
Our arms are strong as thine, to guard them still.
Rather shall your rich city perish first ...

Hector hurled back as good as he got. Ajax was just a blustering great oaf; the Greeks were going to die, cut down around their own ships, and Hector would personally rip Ajax to shreds, carrion for the scavengers. And whooping a savage cry, Hector led the charge, his ranks close packed behind him, Troy's finest; but the Greeks did not waver, facing the assault. And the roar from both brave armies rose up to the heavens, sounding in the halls of the gods.

Book 14
HERA SEDUCES ZEUS

Agamemnon's despair

Resting in the tent where he had tended Machaon, Nestor heard the rising rumble of war. Rushing outside, he was stopped in his tracks by an appalling sight: the great defensive wall breached, his friends beset by the inexorable Trojans; all around him men were hacking, stabbing, flailing, bleeding, dying. Nestor stood, stunned, in two minds—should he take his chariot and dash into the throng, or find Agamemnon?

Just as he had decided to look for the Greek commander, he noticed three figures trailing along the beach, limping and wound-weary: Agamemnon, Odysseus, and Diomedes. They had been resting in their ships, recovering from the fighting, but now they wanted a better view of the state of battle. They leant heavily on their spears, surveying the carnage. When he saw Nestor approaching, Agamemnon had yet another moment of doubt and pain. Why was Nestor turning away from the fighting? Was Hector about to burn the ships, as he had sworn he would? The king dissolved into doleful despair: no one would want to fight, not even to save their own ships, and everyone would hate him, just as Achilles did:

> *Truly I fear lest Hector in his pride*
> *Fulfil the threats he threaten'd loud in Troy,*
> *Never to wind-swept Ilion to return,*
> *Ere he had burnt our ships and slain the crews.*
> *Yea, this will surely now be brought to pass:*
> *For, verily, not less than Peleus' Son,*
> *Hath every gallant warrior through the host*
> *Nursed up a grudge against me, and is loth*
> *To battle, though it be to save his bark.*

Hera seduced Zeus to distract him from the Trojan war while Poseidon helped the Greeks to withstand Hector. Zeus had many lovers, and Hera was jealous of all of them.

Nestor could only agree with Agamemnon. He had no heartlifting words. He suspected that not even Zeus could save them now. Even so, Nestor did not give in that easily—they should make a plan—perhaps a decent strategy would work where brute strength had failed.

Once again, when it came to the crunch, Agamemnon crumbled: it was all hopeless. The wall on which they had relied so heavily had gone; the trench had become a bloodbath for their own men; their losses were unsustainable; and Zeus wanted to kill them all. His plan was that they all just slip away, preferably at night, the boats nearest the sea's edge to go first:

> *Hear therefore, and obey as I enjoin.*
> *The hindmost galleys, nighest to the sea,*
> *These launch forth now upon the sacred deep,*
> *Yet make them, when afloat, to moorings fast,*
> *Till night ambrosial fall, if haply night*
> *Will stay the Trojans from their fierce assail:*
> *Then be the whole fleet launchèd out to sea.*
> *What shame to flee from ruin, though by night?*
> *Better ev'n thus to flee, than captives fall.*

Although not always impressive as a leader of men, Agamemnon's skills as a spearman were never in doubt. At the funeral games for Patroclus, Achilles awarded him the prize for the javelin throw, because he was famously the best in his field.

Odysseus glowered at him. He could not believe his ears. What kind of command was this? Agamemnon was contemptible. He did not deserve to be in command of such armies of brave men. Slinking away, under cover of the night, after all the lives the siege of Troy had cost? A sceptered king, ruling by the divine decree of Zeus, and all he could say was run? Was he mad? It would be handing the Trojans victory on a plate. No Greek soldier would hold the line if he saw his own ships slipping out to sea, abandoning him:

> *I blame thee openly, without restraint,*
> *For this thy rede, who bidd'st us, whilst the war*
> *Hedgeth us round, and in our ears the cry,*
> *To launch our benchèd galleys out to sea:*
> *'Twould be to bring to pass the hopes of Troy,*
> *And draw destruction quicker on our heads.*
> *For surely, when the Achaians saw their ships*
> *Now thrusting out, they must perforce cast back*
> *Their longing eyes and slacken in the fight.*

Agamemnon immediately caved in under the lash of Odysseus' tongue. Of course he was right, but what else could they do? Did anyone else have a plan?

Once again, it was the hothead Diomedes, youngest of the captains, who spoke up, but this time his advice was circumspect. They were all wounded—they would be no help in hand-to-hand fighting, but they could go up to the front lines and offer support, show solidarity, and spur on the faint-hearted. Diomedes' plan was better than nothing, and so they set off toward the fighting, led by Agamemnon.

Poseidon had been watching, and he flew down to Agamemnon's side, offering words of encouragement to the chastened and despairing king. He should forget Achilles—the gods would eventually destroy him; but the gods had not completely washed their hands of Agamemnon—soon he would see with his own eyes the Trojan captains in retreat, rushing back to Troy. Then Poseidon thundered out over the battlefield with a great cry, as loud as ten thousand roaring men, rekindling the lust for battle in every Greek heart.

Hera's plan

Up on her golden throne on Olympus, the queenly Hera looked down and was overjoyed to see her brother Poseidon rallying her beloved Greeks. Then she looked across at Zeus, perched on Mount Ida, oblivious to the battle below, and felt a sudden stab of loathing for him. How could she help? How could she outwit Zeus the mastermind? It occurred to Hera that she possessed assets and weapons that he could never have. She would put on her finery and go to Ida as a beautiful, dutiful wife. With luck, Zeus would be overcome with lust—he had once found her irresistible, so it would not be hard to tempt him again. Then, once they had made love, he would, with a little help, fall into a deep, satisfied, and above all prolonged sleep, which would give Poseidon a chance to help the Greeks to victory.

Pleased with this plan, Hera went to her room, locked the door, and geared up for a battle she knew she could win. She bathed and massaged her skin with sweet oils, dressed her sleek, dark hair, and wrapped herself in a gorgeous robe made from fabric woven by Athena. A tasseled girdle, dazzling silver earrings, and fresh white veils completed the picture. Ready for action, she strode out into the golden hall of Olympus, and beckoned Aphrodite over into a corner where the other gods could not overhear them. Could the dear girl do Hera a favor? Even though they supported opposite sides in the war below? Aphrodite was gracious: of course she

HERA

QUEEN OF OLYMPUS, OLDER SISTER AND CONSORT TO ZEUS, HERA WAS OFTEN JEALOUS OF HER HUSBAND'S OTHER LOVERS, AS WELL AS HIS CHILDREN, AND REBELLED AGAINST HIS AUTHORITY REGULARLY. SHE FOUGHT FIERCELY FOR THE GREEKS DURING THE TROJAN WAR, RISKING ZEUS' WRATH. HERA LOATHED THE TROJANS, BECAUSE PARIS HAD SLIGHTED HER WHEN HE AWARDED THE PRIZE FOR THE FAIREST TO APHRODITE.

HERACLES

HERACLES WAS THE SON OF ZEUS AND ALCMENA. HERA WAS RAGINGLY JEALOUS OF HIM, AND TRIED TO KILL HIM IN HIS CRADLE, AND WHEN THAT FAILED, TO RUIN OR DESTROY HIM AT EVERY OPPORTUNITY. HERACLES WAS NO FRIEND OF TROY; HE RESCUED LAOMEDON'S DAUGHTER HESIONE FROM A SEA MONSTER SENT BY POSEIDON, BUT LAOMEDON RENEGED ON THE AGREED PAYMENT, SO AFTER HE HAD COMPLETED HIS LABORS, HERACLES CAME BACK AND DESTROYED THE CITY WALLS, WITH THE HELP OF TELAMON, FATHER OF GREAT AJAX.

would help—Hera was queen of the gods, after all. So Hera lied brazenly and fluently. She said she wanted Aphrodite to lend her the gifts of love and sweet desire, to take to her foster-mother Tethys, who had quarreled so badly with her husband Ocean that they were estranged. Hera desperately wanted to reconcile them, to help them fall in love again. She was even smart enough to give herself a motive no one would ever question—she wanted them to honor her:

> And I would quench the broil, wherewith long while
> They hold from their mutual love's delights.
> For, should my prayer win way into their hearts,
> Should I unite them by old bond again,
> They love and honour me for evermore.

How could the goddess of love refuse such a request? Especially as it was made by the queen of heaven herself. Instantly, Aphrodite took off the girdle she always wore, the magic sash woven with love and longing and soft whispering, designed to drive men mad with desire, and gave it to Hera. With this talisman Hera could not fail.

> Take therefore, in thy bosom lay this zone:
> Closed in its broidery all witchery lies;
> Thus arm'd, whate'er thy heart's desire may be,
> I promise that thou shall not seek in vain.

Hera gave a smile of sincere gratitude and tied the sash around herself. As Aphrodite drifted languidly back to the halls of Olympus, Hera sped off to the island of Lemnos, halfway between Troy and the home of the gods. There she met Sleep, the twin brother of Death. Clasping his hand, and flattering him outrageously, she now begged him to do her a favor—to put Zeus to sleep. Hera offered a sumptuous reward—a solid golden throne, hand-crafted by the gods' own blacksmith:

> ... When soon I lie
> With Zeus embracing, steep beneath their lids
> His shining eyes in slumber; grant me this;
> And I will give to thee a throne of gold,
> Fair, incorruptible, the Halt-foot's work,
> Hephaestus: he shall frame the step, whereon
> Thou may'st in revel rest thy glistening feet.

Sleep laughed lazily. Hera must be joking. He could put anyone and anything to sleep, but not Zeus; he had already done so once at Hera's command, as part of her plan to destroy Heracles, and Zeus had come after him in a towering rage. Sleep had only been saved by fleeing to the safety of Night.

Hera redoubled her efforts. Sleep was being overcautious; of course Zeus would not get so angry about Hera interfering in a war waged by mere mortals as he had done when she had attacked his own son. And then Hera offered a much better reward—one of the younger graces, Pasithea, as a wife. Hera had hit the button. Sleep had been lusting after Pasithea for many years. Even so, he wanted a copper-bottomed deal. He made Hera swear on the River Styx, and by the first gods, the Titans, that Pasithea would be his. They quickly sealed their bargain with oaths, then both set off for Mount Ida. Sleep got there first, slipping unseen past Zeus and shinning nimbly up a pine tree, where he settled down hidden among the branches, disguised as a hawk.

Hera climbed up the mountain, making sure that Zeus could see her. When he set eyes on her, Zeus was overcome with lust, and the memory of lust, of their first time, a long time ago. He stopped Hera and asked where she was going in such a hurry. Where were her chariot and horses? Hera answered demurely with the same story she had used to fool Aphrodite. She was on an errand of matrimonial mercy to Ocean and Tethys. Her chariot was at the foot of the mountain; she had just come up to check with Zeus that it would be all right to go—she did not want him to think she was going behind his back. Zeus took her hand and smiled lasciviously. What was the hurry? It could wait until tomorrow. Why didn't she come to bed? She was making him weak with desire, he had never felt such irresistible longing—not for any of the goddesses or women he had ever bedded, not even for herself, the Hera he had known before.

Hera pretended to be taken aback. Surely the great Zeus did not mean them to make love on the bare peak of Mount Ida where the whole world could see them? She would be so ashamed. Could they not at least go to Zeus' own chamber? But Zeus could not wait any longer, he would wrap them in golden clouds so thick that not even the sun could pierce them, no one would see them, he must have her now. And Zeus caught Hera up in his arms, spinning clouds around her; flowers blossomed and green grass sprouted where they lay, cocooned in a golden mist. And soon Zeus was clasped in Hera's arms, lust sated, all passion spent, in deep, warm, luxurious oblivion. Sleep had done his work well.

THE GRACES

A GROUP OF MINOR GODDESSES ASSOCIATED WITH APHRODITE. THEIR NAMES VARIED, AS DID THEIR NUMBER, BUT THERE WERE ALWAYS AT LEAST THREE, AND THEY WERE EMBODIMENTS OF BEAUTY, GENTLENESS, AND FRIENDSHIP. PASITHEA, THE GRACE PROMISED TO SLEEP BY HERA, WAS POSSIBLY AN INVENTION OF HOMER'S. THE GRACES' PARENTS WERE PROBABLY ZEUS AND EURYNOME, A DAUGHTER OF OCEAN AND TETHYS.

Poseidon seizes the moment

O nce Zeus slept, Sleep rushed off to find Poseidon by the hollow ships and tell him what had happened:

> *Poseidon, now vouchsafe thy strongest help,*
> *And, though it be but for a little space,*
> *Increase the fame to Argos, whilst Zeus lies*
> *Fast-bound; whom I have wrapp'd in softest cloud,*
> *And Herè to her love's embrace hath guiled.*

Poseidon lost no time. Striding to the front of the ranks, he harangued the Greeks. Were they just going to hand over victory to Hector? Hector was counting on Achilles staying out of the fight, locked in his cage of anger, but they didn't need Achilles:

> *Yield we, Argeians, yield we victory*
> *To Priameian Hector—to destroy*
> *Our galleys, and to win immortal name?*
> *He threats this loud, and vaunts, because he knows*
> *Achilles in his ship, for wrath removed.*
> *Yet, if we each would fire the other on,*
> *Him we might lack, nor feel it overmuch.*

The Greek captains were glad to obey. Despite their wounds, Diomedes, Odysseus, and Agamemnon marshaled their men, and following Poseidon's instructions, they all swapped armor according to merit—the best fighters took the best armor and the worst took the worst. And Poseidon led them into battle, in his hand a long bright sword like a lightning bolt, the very sight of which put the fear of the gods into mortal men—no one could survive such a blade.

On the Trojan side, Hector rallied his troops. And the two battle lines came together, the one led by Hector, the other by the god of earthquakes, wave smashing on wave with a noise like the roar of wildfire, or the howl of a hurricane. Hector went into action immediately, hurling his spear at Great Ajax. He scored a direct hit, square in the chest, but the weapon hit the point where the shield and sword strap crossed, and bounced off harmlessly. Angry at this missed opportunity, Hector backed off, but Ajax, enraged, snatched up an enormous rock—one of the mooring stones that secured the ships—and flung it at Hector, striking his throat. The force of the blow spun Hector around and sent him reeling to the earth. A screaming mob of Greeks charged in for the kill, but before any of their spears could strike, Hector's comrades—Agenor and Polydamas, Aeneas and Sarpedon and Glaucus, and all their squadrons—sprang to his defense, forming an impenetrable ring of shields around their fallen captain. Behind the shield wall, Hector was carried away from the fighting to where his chariot and driver were waiting.

Beside themselves with joy at seeing the Trojan commander laid low, the Greeks renewed their attack. First to strike was Little Ajax, spearing Satnius in the side, knocking him over. Greeks and Trojans swarmed together over the body. Polydamas, bent on revenge, speared Prothoenor, the Boeotian commander, through the shoulder, then crowed over his victim, boasting that he had given him a crutch to help him on his way to Hades. Great Ajax hurled his spear at the jubilant Polydamas, but the Trojan dodged sideways, and the shaft hit Archilochus, slicing through his spine at the neck. Now it was Ajax's turn to crow; his victim had been one of Antenor's many sons, Antenor, Priam's most trusted counselor. Wasn't this a fine revenge for Prothoenor?

The warriors traded blow for blow in bloody strife, each man determined to avenge his fallen comrades. The Greek Peneleos launched his spear at Acamas, who turned to run; the spear found a home in the eye socket of Ilioneus instead, plunging through and out at the back of his neck. Peneleos took his sharp sword and mercifully lopped off Ilioneus' head; still in its helmet, it tumbled onto the ground, the long spear stuck in the eye socket. Peneleos grabbed the spear shaft and brandished the trophy in the air like some ghastly flower on a stalk, taunting the Trojans:

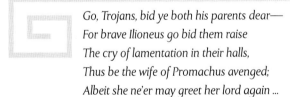

Go, Trojans, bid ye both his parents dear—
For brave Ilioneus go bid them raise
The cry of lamentation in their halls,
Thus be the wife of Promachus avenged;
Albeit she ne'er may greet her lord again ...

For the first time, without Hector to lead them and exhort them on, the Trojans began to doubt themselves, and fear gripped them.

So what was the score, once Poseidon had turned the tide of battle in favor of the Greeks? Great Ajax brought down Hyrtius, commander of the Mysians; Antilochus killed Phalces and Mermerus; Meriones saw to Morys and Hippotion; Teucer cut down Periphetes and Protoon; Menelaus slayed Hyperenor. But it was Little Ajax who killed the most, for no one could run down a fleeing victim as swiftly as he could.

LITTLE AJAX

THE SON OF OÏLEUS, LITTLE AJAX, ONE OF HELEN'S SUITORS, LED A CONTINGENT OF 40 SHIPS FROM LOCRIS. ALSO KNOWN AS OILEAN AJAX OR LESSER AJAX, LITTLE AJAX WAS SO CALLED BECAUSE, IN CONTRAST TO GREAT AJAX HE WAS PHYSICALLY SMALL, BUT WAS A FIERCE FIGHTER, EXPERT WITH THE SPEAR AND AT RUNNING HIS ENEMY DOWN. HOWEVER, HIS ARROGANCE MADE THE GODS HATE HIM, ESPECIALLY ATHENA, WHOSE TEMPLE HE DESECRATED AFTER TROY HAD FALLEN; SHE PERSUADED ZEUS AND POSEIDON TO SINK HIS SHIP AND DROWN HIM ON HIS WAY HOME.

Book 15
ZEUS REGROUPS

Strife among the gods

INSTANT *ILIAD*

INSTANT *ILIAD*

JUST AS THE GREEKS
ARE GETTING THE
UPPER HAND, ZEUS
WAKES UP FROM HIS
LUST-INDUCED SLEEP.
WHEN HE SEES WHAT IS
HAPPENING ON THE
BATTLEFIELD, HE FLIES
INTO A RAGE, AND
THREATENS ALL THE
GODS IF THEY
INTERFERE WITH HIS
DIVINE PLAN AGAIN.
POSEIDON BACKS
DOWN AND
ABANDONS THE
GREEKS, AND APOLLO
DRIVES HECTOR ON,
PROTECTING THE
TROJANS WITH ZEUS'
AEGIS. THE GREEKS ARE
DRIVEN BACK, ONE
STEP AT A TIME, UNTIL
THEY ARE FIGHTING
ON THE DECKS OF
THEIR SHIPS.

The Greeks were driving the Trojans back, back past the jutting stakes and over the trench, hacking them down in droves—and then Zeus awoke. Leaping to his feet, he stared thunderstruck at the sight of the Trojan rout, Poseidon triumphant at the head of the Greek charge, Hector knocked out and struggling for breath. He rounded on Hera. What had she done?

> *Thy craft it is, thy malice unrepress'd*
> *Disloyal Herè, that hath made cease*
> *The noble Hector from the fray, and fill'd*
> *His people with this panic. Scarce I know*
> *But that the first-fruits of this evil guile*
> *Shall be thine own to taste, and I once more*
> *Shall lash thee with my scourge.*

Did she not remember how he had punished her, and any god who had helped her, when she had tried to destroy his son Heracles? If she didn't, it would be a pleasure to remind her, and she need not think that her seduction techniques would save her then. Hera shrank back from Zeus, quaking with fear, but still trying to wheedle her way out of trouble. She swore by everything sacred—Earth, Sky, the river Styx, by Zeus himself, even by their still-warm marriage bed—that it was not she who had persuaded Poseidon to go down and fight with the Greeks; it must have been his own rage against the Trojans that made him do it, and pity for those who honored him... of course, had she known, she would have made every effort to dissuade him, and force him to accept Zeus' command.

Zeus smiled sardonically. To make it clear who was in charge, he ordered Hera to go to Olympus and send Iris, the gods' messenger, and Apollo to him. Once again Zeus outlined to Hera his grand, terrible strategy: to help the Trojans batter the Greeks back until Achilles was drawn into the fighting. Achilles would kill Hector. Then the Trojans and their city would be utterly destroyed, and Achilles would win everlasting glory, as Zeus had promised Thetis. Zeus was even going to sacrifice his own son, Sarpedon, to make this possible:

> *Then shall he [Hector] smite Achaia's sons with fear,*
> *Till routed on Achilles' barks they fall:*
> *Achilles next shall send Patroclus forth,*
> *To fall at last by Hector, yet to slay*
> *Full many a manly warrior ere he falls—*
> *My son, mine own Sarpedon, with the rest:*
> *Wroth for Patroclus, shall Achilles then*
> *Slay noble Hector. And, from that day forth,*
> *Ev'n till the Achaians by Athene's help*
> *Take the proud steep of Ilion, unto Troy*
> *Rout I ordain and unredeem'd defeat.*

But until Achilles fought, and Hector fell, no god—or goddess—was to lift a finger on behalf of the Greeks.

Zeus allowed the gods to take sides in the war, and the Olympians seized the opportunity to fight among themselves, settling past slights and old scores.

If any one of them stepped out of line, Zeus would destroy them all.

Trouble on Olympus

Quick as thought, and anxious to be out of Zeus' sight, Hera fled to Olympus. As she entered the hall, the other gods crowded round curiously, but she brushed them all aside, and would only talk to Themis who brought her a cup of wine. Fortified, Hera took her seat in the great hall, and smiled grimly before speaking. The gods had been mad to defy Zeus; he cared nothing for them. Take Ares, for example— did he not know that his son Ascalaphus had died on the killing fields below?

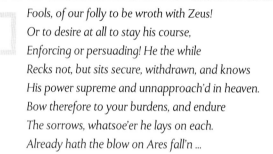

Fools, of our folly to be wroth with Zeus!
Or to desire at all to stay his course,
Enforcing or persuading! He the while
Recks not, but sits secure, withdrawn, and knows
His power supreme and unapproach'd in heaven.
Bow therefore to your burdens, and endure
The sorrows, whatsoe'er he lays on each.
Already hath the blow on Ares fall'n ...

Horrified, Ares smacked his great hands down on his thighs, and bellowed in anguish. Who could blame him if he went down to the Greek ships to avenge his son—so what if Zeus crushed him with a thunderbolt so that he lay in the dust and blood with dead men? Without stopping to think, Ares began pulling on his armor, calling to his henchmen, Fear and Panic, to get his war chariot ready. The other gods stood aghast, but Athena leaped up from her throne and tore Ares' helmet from his great shaggy head, plucking the shield from his arm, and the spear from his great fist. Was he insane? Did he not understand what Hera had just said? If any one of them stepped out of line, Zeus would abandon his games down among mortals, and destroy them all. Better men than Ares' son had died—they could not save every mortal; he must let it go. And Athena pushed Ares back into his seat. The gods fell silent. Gloomily, Hera dispatched Iris and Apollo to Zeus, as he had commanded.

Poseidon rebuffed

Iris and Apollo flew to Mount Ida, where they found Zeus in a rather better temper now that everyone was obeying him once more. He sent Iris to Poseidon to command him to stop fighting and go home. If he refused, Iris was to remind him that Zeus was the first-born, the far greater god. Sure enough, when Iris delivered Zeus' orders, Poseidon exploded. How dare Zeus try to intimidate him? They were equal—he, Zeus, and Hades—they each owned a third of the world. He was not at his brother's beck and call like a child:

> *I move not therefore by the breath of Zeus:*
> *Content within his portion let him dwell;*
> *Nor with his strength, for all it be so great,*
> *Threat me as in his bondage. Let him chide*
> *The sons and daughters whom himself begat,*
> *With these loud words;—they needs must brook his will,*
> *And, force-perforce, obey;—but leave me free!*

Iris was diplomatic. Did Poseidon really want her to take this curt rejection back to Zeus? Had Poseidon forgotten about the Furies? They always sided with the first-born and to repent was a noble act.

Poseidon sighed and climbed down. It came to something when a messenger was more noble-minded than a god. He would bow this time, although it hurt him when Zeus tried to dominate; but he had a message in return. If, in the end, Zeus denied the Greeks victory, and Troy did not fall, then Poseidon's rage would be unstoppable:

> *Howbeit, I bow me to his will this while*
> *Obedient, and depart. But this thing more*
> *Tell him, and from my soul the threat proceeds:*
> *If, against me, and thwarting Herè's will,*
> *And Pallas, gatherer of the spoils in war,*
> *And Hermes, and Hephaestus, Kings in heaven,*
> *He spares proud Ilion's towers, nor grants her fall,*
> *But takes the mastery from Achaia's sons,*
> *So be it—yet this warning let him weigh;*
> *The wrath between us two shall ne'er be heal'd.*

THE THREE BROTHER GODS

ZEUS, POSEIDON, AND HADES WERE THE THREE MOST IMPORTANT SONS OF RHEA AND CRONOS. CRONOS DEVOURED ALL HIS CHILDREN, TO PREVENT THEM FROM TAKING POWER FROM HIM. RHEA MANAGED TO RESCUE ZEUS, THE YOUNGEST, AND HE IN TURN RESCUED ALL THE OTHERS. THEY JOINED TOGETHER TO KILL THEIR FATHER. THE WORLD WAS DIVIDED INTO THREE: ZEUS TOOK THE SKY, POSEIDON THE SEA, AND HADES, THE UNDERWORLD. THE EARTH, AND THE MORTALS ON IT, WAS COMMON GROUND. ALTHOUGH THE BROTHERS WERE MEANT TO HAVE EQUAL STATUS, ZEUS CLAIMED SUPERIORITY, BECAUSE HE WAS THE FIRST TO BE RESCUED.

Honor only partly satisfied, and still angry with his overbearing brother god, Poseidon withdrew from the battlefield, diving back into the sea. The earth shook at his departure. Suddenly the Greek heroes felt heartsick and bereft.

Apollo rides with Hector

As Poseidon sank, Zeus gave Apollo his fearsome battle shield, his tasseled aegis, and sent him down to Hector, to rouse his courage:

> But take my fringèd Aegis in thy hands;
> Shake it abroad, and therewithal affright
> The Danaan* heroes; whilst thyself, my son,
> Tendest on noble Hector. Raise him up;
> Imbreathe thy might within him; till he drive
> The Danaans to their ships and shore repell'd.
>
> * Danaans = Greeks

Apollo found Hector by the river. By now he was sitting up and taking notice, but still finding it hard to breathe; he had thought he was on his way to Hades. Apollo announced that Hector must get his charioteers lined up and ready. They were going to make a headlong dash to the Greek ships, with Apollo charging before them, clearing the way. Instantly revitalized, Hector leaped up like a well-fed young stallion, eager to get to his mares. He ran up and down the lines tirelessly, organizing his troops.

AEGIS

THIS SACRED OBJECT, ALSO KNOWN AS A STORM SHIELD OR BATTLE SHIELD, BELONGED TO ZEUS. IN THE *ILIAD* IT WAS USED ON BOTH SIDES, BY ATHENA AND APOLLO, TO SHOW THAT THEY WIELDED THE AUTHORITY OF ZEUS. ATHENA SOMETIMES WORE IT AROUND HER NECK, SO IT WAS NOT RIGID, BUT FLEXIBLE, LIKE CHAIN MAIL. THE WORD AEGIS MEANS "GOATSKIN." DESCRIBED AS GLEAMING, AND FRINGED WITH TASSELS, IT HAS AN IMAGE OF THE GORGON MEDUSA AT ITS CENTER AND MADE THE NOISE OF A THOUSAND THUNDERSTORMS, PUTTING FEAR INTO THE HEART OF THE ENEMY.

The Greeks had been pressing on in close formation, sure of their victory, when suddenly they saw Hector appear, reborn it seemed, and more powerful than ever. Fear clutched at their souls, and their hearts failed them. Only one warrior kept his head. Thoas the young Aetolian commander tried to rally them. Hector may have sprung back to life, but that was all the more reason to try to bring him down permanently; they should send the rank and file back to the ships, and those of them who considered themselves heroes should work together to take out the blazing Trojan menace:

> Hear, therefore, and obey ye this my word.
> Back on their galleys let the host retire;
> Whilst we, who boast chief prowess in the camp,
> Level our lances firm, and steadfast stand
> In phalanx to repel him, face to face;
> For, let his fury be whate'er it may,
> On us so gather'd he will fear to charge.

Great Ajax, Idomeneus, Teucer, Meriones, and Meges, and their comrades closed up in tight formation, spears at the ready. But storming at them came the Trojans, and at their head ran Apollo, holding Zeus' terrible shield in his outstretched arms, the shield made by Hephaestus to put the fear of the gods into mortals. Spears and arrows flew thick and fast, but the Greeks stood their ground until Apollo was close enough to stare directly into their eyes. When he shook the tasseled aegis at them, it sucked the valor from their hearts, leaving them stumbling around in blind panic, like cattle attacked in the night by wild beasts.

At their head ran Apollo, holding Zeus' terrible battle shield in his outstretched arms.

Apollo led the Trojan assault on the Greeks' defenses, brandishing Zeus' battle shield to blind, deafen, and terrorize the Greeks. Walls, ramparts, and ditches meant nothing to the god, who destroyed them with a careless kick, leaving the way clear for Hector and his forces to reach the ships.

The rampart falls

The tight Greek formations dissolved into hand-to-hand fighting. The Trojans laid about them; within minutes, many Greek captains—Arcelisaus, Stichius, Iasus, Mecisteus, Echius, Clonius, Deiochus, and Medon, half brother to Little Ajax—lay dead. And while the Trojans ransacked the corpses, those remaining Greeks abandoned their dead comrades, scrambling mad with fear, through the trench and back to their crumbling rampart. Hector shouted to his men not to waste time looting—they must get to the ships and burn them. He lashed them on, and on they ran behind Apollo, who loped ahead, carelessly pulling down the earth walls of the Greek trench, making a dike wide enough for the Trojans to charge across. When they reached the rampart, Apollo kicked it down as easily as a child kicks over a sandcastle, and the Greeks looked on in horror and despair as all their hard work and hope was destroyed.

Now there was stampede as the Greeks ran witless back to their ships, everyone gibbering in panic and praying to the gods. Nestor beseeched Zeus to remember all the sacrifices that had been made in his honor, not to let the Greeks be run down in ignominy. Zeus heard him, and sent a thunderbolt, but the Trojans took it as a signal to them, and threw themselves even more fiercely into the fight. Driving their chariots right up to the first line of ships, they forced the Greeks to climb up onto the decks and fight from there, using the great bronze-tipped pikes kept for sea battles.

Patroclus was in Eurypylus' tent, tending his friend's wounds, but when as he heard the tumult as the wall fell, he leaped up; he had to go to Achilles, to try to persuade him to fight at last, now the enemy was on the ships.

Hector and Great Ajax

The fighting had reached stalemate; the Greeks, outnumbered, could not fight off the Trojans; but the Trojans found it difficult to maneuver in the narrow gaps that ran between the ships. In the midst of all this, Hector and Ajax confronted each other, slogging it out over a single ship. As they fought, Hector's cousin Caletor thrust his way through with a flaming torch in his hand, intent on setting fire to the vessel. Ajax stopped him short with a vicious spear thrust. Calling for comrades to defend Caletor's body, Hector hurled his spear at Ajax, but missed, bringing down Lycophron, Ajax's brother instead. Immediately, Ajax yelled for Teucer, who fired off a salvo of arrows at the Trojans. He brought down Clitius, the driver of Polydamas' chariot, but then concentrated his fire power on Hector, aiming at the great warrior's dazzling bronze helmet. Teucer would have found his mark, and stopped the battle right there, but Zeus snapped his bowstring and the arrow clattered impotently to the ground. Teucer was disgusted. The gods were turning their own weapons against them. Dropping the useless bow, he snatched up a spear and shield, and joined Ajax in the ranks.

When Hector saw Teucer abandon his weapon of choice, he knew that the gods were indeed on his side, and seized the opportunity to boost his men's morale—the Trojans could not lose:

> Close your ranks therefore; flinch not in the fight
> Amongst these galleys. And, if any fall
> By sword or javelin, to his hour of death
> Brought in this battle, let him die content:
> So standing for his country's sake to die,
> Is no unworthy thing; and he shall leave
> His wife and children safe thereby, and home
> And land unminish'd; when Achaia's sons
> Sail to their own dear country driven at last.

Ajax tried to drown out Hector's rallying speech with one of his own. Did the Greeks want Hector to take their ships? Were they planning to walk home? They had better fight with all their fury—Hector meant what he said, he was not inviting them to a dance:

> Expect ye, when ye once have lost the ships,
> To walk the roaring waters dry-foot home?
> Or are ye deaf to bright-helm'd Hector's shouts,
> Threatening to burn the galleys, and with cheers
> Kindling his host? His voice is loud enow:
> To no sweet dance that summons, but to war
> Nor have we better counsel in our power,
> Than, might and main, to meet him, front to front.

With both sides fired up, the slaughter began again, Trojan on Greek, Greek on Trojan. Hector slew Schidius—Ajax killed Laodamas, another son of Antenor; the Trojan Polydamas finished off Outus—Meges lunged at Polydamas but hit Croesmus; Meges

SEA PIKES

WHEN GREAT AJAX FOUGHT ON THE DECKS OF THE SHIP, HE COULD NOT USE STANDARD WEAPONS BECAUSE THEY WERE TOO SHORT TO REPEL BOARDERS, BUT INSTEAD USED GREAT BRONZE-TIPPED PIKES FOR SEA BATTLES. THE PIKES WERE LONG AND HEAVY, USUALLY DEPLOYED BY TWO OR MORE MEN; SO AJAX DEMONSTRATED HIS GREAT STRENGTH BY USING ONE SO EFFECTIVELY ALONE.

and Menelaus working together brought down Dolops, the Trojans' crack spearsman, and fell upon him, prizing off his armor. Hector and Melanippus rushed to defend him, while Ajax urged his troops to steel themselves, hold fast, and stick together. They raised their shields together, a solid wall of brass. Antilochus, spurred on by Menelaus, leaped out from the ranks, glaring left and right, spear poised, locking onto his target Melanippus. He brought him down, but was driven off his prey by Hector.

Determined to impose his will, Zeus inflamed the Trojans while blasting the spirit out of the Greeks. His heart was set finally on getting Hector to burn the ships, so that he could make good his promise to Thetis. Once the ships were on fire, he would thrust the Trojans back ignominiously, and give glory to the Greeks. So he drove Hector on, although the Trojan had enough rage of his own—he was like Ares himself, eyes flashing flame, his terrible spear shaking in his grip. And Zeus defended his champion all the harder because he knew that Hector's life was short—it would not be long until he fell to Achilles.

Hector reaches the ships

The Greeks closed ranks, but they could not withstand the might of Hector, crashing down on them, it seemed from all sides, like the relentless pounding of a perfect storm. The Greeks skittered away from him as best they could, but he brought down Periphetes, who tripped over his own shield, staking him through the heart as he lay, and none of his comrades dared defend his body, so afraid were they of the mighty Hector.

Gradually, the Trojans beat the Greeks back through the first row of the ships to their tents beyond. Here discipline re-asserted itself, and the Greeks rallied, held to the line by shame and fear. Nestor shouted words of encouragement:

Be men, my friends, and hold your honour dear.
Bethink ye of your name's repute elsewhere;
But above all let every man remember
His own dear wife and children, land and home
And his own parents (whether these be dead
Or living still)—yea , in their names I plead,
Whose voices far away ye cannot hear—
Stand bravely still, nor turn to craven flight.

SHIP DEPLOYMENT

AROUND 1,000 SHIPS SAILED TO TROY, ALTHOUGH NOT ALL AT ONCE. HOW THEY WERE DRAWN UP ALONG THE BEACH IS NOT VERY CLEAR IN THE *ILIAD*. THEY WERE ALL BEACHED WITH THEIR STERNS FACING INLAND, SO THEY WERE READY TO DEPART. PROBABLY MORE THAN ONE ROW DEEP. THE SHIPS BELONGING TO AGAMEMNON, ODYSSEUS, AND DIOMEDES WERE THE FIRST TO LAND. PROBABLY QUITE FAR UP THE BEACH. THE REST OF THE FLEET WAS ARRANGED ON EACH SIDE OF THEM, VERY CLOSE TOGETHER, SO THAT FIGHTING BETWEEN THEM WAS DIFFICULT.

Athena chose that moment to disperse the fog of war; a hard bright light shone across the battlefield, and the Greeks could see in terrible clarity Hector, and all his troops, and the battalions drawn up in reserve behind them. It froze their blood. But Great Ajax was not daunted. He leaped up onto the deck of the nearest ship and seized one of the huge sea-fighting pikes; using it as a balancing pole, he leaped from ship to ship like a daredevil rider jumping from one of his team of galloping horses to the next, all the time yelling at his men to defend their ships and their tents.

Hector swooped down on the ships like a raptor, his troops behind him, full of fresh strength and energy, as if they were new to the fight. He felt the great hand of Zeus propelling him along. Trojan hearts sang, secure in victory, but the Greeks fought on, doomed, convinced they would all die, yet desperate for honor. A boiling sea of warriors swirled and chopped and hacked around the hulls—no more spears and arrows, now was the time for close combat, for long knives, short swords, and brutal axes; dropped and shattered blades littered the ground and men slithered in blood and sand. At last, Hector reached the ship that had belonged to Protesilaus. He clung with both arms to the horn of the high stern, bellowing to the Trojans to bring fire, the ships were theirs. He had always thought that attacking the ships was the only way to win—and now, poor fool, he believed that Zeus was granting him a famous victory:

> *Now bring ye fire, and let your shouts go up*
> *Together; Zeus bestows at last a day*
> *That pays us all our pains—ev'n to destroy*
> *These galleys: which, though all devoid they came*
> *Of Heaven's good-will, no less have wrought us hurt,*
> *Uncheck'd, because our elders in their fears*
> *Would still detain me, when I would advance,*
> *And with me held our host behind the walls.*
> *But, though Zeus blinded so our sense awhile,*
> *Now his own spirit impels and bids us on.*

And the Trojans threw themselves at the ships. Ajax was forced down from the stern to the foredeck, bracing himself by the mast, desperately wielding his great pike to repel anyone foolhardy enough to come near the ship with a torch, and screaming defiance at the enemy. He urged on his comrades—they were alone now, their backs to the sea, strangers in a strange land, with no great walled city to run home to. He fought like a madman, skewering any who came near—twelve men he impaled that day as they fought to reach and burn his ship.

Trojan hearts sang, secure in victory.

Book 16
THE DEATH OF PATROCLUS

Patroclus pleads with Achilles

INSTANT *ILIAD*

AS THE BATTLE RAGES AROUND THE SHIPS, PATROCLUS GOES TO ACHILLES AND REPORTS THE DISASTER THAT IS THREATENING THE GREEKS. ACHILLES IS PERSUADED TO SEND PATROCLUS AND THE MYRMIDONS TO REINFORCE THE GREEK ARMY, BUT WARNS PATROCLUS NOT TO VENTURE AS FAR AS THE CITY FOR FEAR OF ENCOUNTERING ONE OF THE HOSTILE GODS. DRAWN INTO THE HEAT OF BATTLE, PATROCLUS FORGETS THIS WARNING AND MEETS HIS FATE.

Leaving Eurypylus and the Greek fleet, Patroclus stumbled in tears to the tent of Achilles, who was astonished to see him weeping like a little girl and asked him the cause of his distress. Was there some terrible news from home? Or was Patroclus grief-stricken because the Greeks were being slaughtered, all as a result of Agamemnon's presumption in offending the Greeks' finest warrior? Patroclus, distraught, told Achilles of the appalling Greek losses, and could not stop himself from attacking his friend for failing to prevent their humiliation:

> Smitten with spears or arrows, all, who late
> Were bravest in the fight, lie cabin'd now;
> Tydeus' brave Son is by an arrow pierced,
> And likewise through the hip Eurypylus;
> But spears have struck Odysseus and the King:
> To whom the leeches minister, and stanch
> Their wounds; but thou, Achilles, sitt'st unmoved.
> Such wrath, as this thou nursest, ne'er be mine!

Patroclus pleaded with Achilles at least to let him take some of the Myrmidons into the battle, and to lend him his armor so that the Trojans would be deceived into thinking that Achilles had returned. In asking this, Patroclus sealed his fate.

Achilles was greatly disturbed by the news of the Trojan advance, and although he couldn't resist pointing out once more that all this was Agamemnon's fault, he recalled his promise to help the Greeks if the fighting reached the hollow ships. And so Achilles agreed to Patroclus' request. He knew that the Trojans would not have

Patroclus was killed by Hector, but he had help: Apollo made him vulnerable by removing his helmet, shattering his spear, and loosening his shield straps. Euphorbus stabbed him in the back with his spear; only then could Hector finish him off.

Hector and his troops finally broke through the Greek lines and managed to set fire to one of the ships; this had been Hector's plan all along. Without ships, the Greeks would have no escape route, and no supply lines, and the Trojans could massacre them at their leisure.

reached the ships if they had seen his helmet glinting in the midst of the battle. As it was, Achilles couldn't even hear the loathsome Agamemnon shouting orders—the only voice to be heard was Hector's. He charged Patroclus to win back his honor, so that the Greeks would be minded to return his beautiful Briseis. Then Achilles gave Patroclus a warning: he was to win the victory at the ships, but then leave the other Greeks to do the fighting on the plain. If Patroclus went out across the plain to the city he risked being taken on by one of the gods who loved the Trojans. Achilles wanted to be sure that he and his dear friend would escape from the slaughter.

While Achilles and Patroclus were negotiating, Great Ajax realized that he could no longer sustain his position in the stern of the ship. His shoulder was aching from holding up his shield to ward off the blows that rained on him, and the sweat was pouring from his limbs. One slash from Hector's sword removed the head and point of his spear, and Ajax recognized that the gods were taking a hand on the Trojan side. He fell back and the Trojans swarmed in, throwing torches into the ship. A moment later it was on fire from stem to stern.

Seeing the flames, Achilles hurried Patroclus into his armor and went to assemble the Myrmidons. One by one, Patroclus donned Achilles' gleaming breastplate and close-fitting greaves, and the helmet with the horsehair plume. He strapped on his sword and slung the shield over his shoulder, leaving behind only Achilles' mighty spear, which nobody but its owner was able to wield. Soon the Myrmidons were ready too, lining up behind Patroclus' chariot. Achilles addressed the assembly, reminding them of the threats they had made against the Trojans while he was nursing his rage. Now was their chance to put them into effect. Then Achilles went to the back of his tent and retrieved from his inlaid chest the beautiful cup used for libations to the gods. He poured the wine onto the ground as a sacrifice, praying to Zeus that Patroclus should strike a blow against the Trojans and would come home unscathed:

Strengthen his soul, that Hector too may know
Him my brave follower able well alone
To bear the battle, and may judge, if then
Himself will range in fury still unharm'd,
When I move forth into the moil of war.
And grant that, when he soon hath chased away
The tumult and the rout from off the fleet,
Unscathed may he return amongst these barks,
Safe with mine arms, and these my gallant men.

Having replaced the cup in the chest, Achilles came back out to watch the Myrmidons advance into action. Patroclus exhorted them to win glory for Achilles and to put Agamemnon to shame for not giving him proper respect.

The return of the Myrmidons

Arriving at the battlefield, the Myrmidons rushed at the Trojans with a roar. Seeing Patroclus in that shining armor, the Trojan front ranks were convinced that the fearsome Achilles had returned to the fray. They began to waver, every warrior glancing around to see some way of escape. When the Myrmidon line came within range of the Trojans, Patroclus hurled his spear, causing panic and confusion among

PATROCLUS

THE GREEK WARRIOR WHO WAS BROUGHT UP IN THE HOUSE OF ACHILLES' FATHER AND BECAME ACHILLES' PASSIONATE FRIEND AND THE OBJECT OF ACHILLES' LOVE. HE FOUGHT BRAVELY AGAINST THE TROJANS UNTIL ACHILLES LEFT THE BATTLE IN A SULK, AND PATROCLUS WENT WITH HIM. BUT IT WAS PATROCLUS WHO FIRST PERSUADED ACHILLES AT LEAST TO LET HIM GO BACK INTO THE BATTLE IN HIS PLACE— WITH DISASTROUS RESULTS. THE TWO OF THEM WERE REUNITED IN THE UNDERWORLD.

GLAUCUS

LIKE SARPEDON, GLAUCUS WAS A PRINCE FROM LYCIA, WHICH WAS AN ALLY OF THE TROJANS IN THE WAR. HE LED THE LYCIAN TROOPS INTO BATTLE DRESSED IN GOLDEN ARMOR, AS BEFITTED THE GRANDSON OF BELLEROPHON THE LEGENDARY SUPERHERO (SEE PAGE 64). BOTH SARPEDON AND GLAUCUS WERE DESTINED TO BE KILLED IN THE FIGHTING—BUT NOT BEFORE GLAUCUS MANAGED TO BEFRIEND THE GREEK WARRIOR DIOMEDES ON THE BATTLEFIELD AND TO SWAP ARMOR WITH HIM.

them and driving them backward from the burning ships. Patroclus and his men stopped to put out the flames, leaving the embers damp and smoldering, before resuming the bloody pursuit of the Trojans.

One by one, the Greeks began to pick off the Trojan leaders in the front line, and as they were killed, the fight began to go out of those around them. Great Ajax was determined to strike at Hector with his spear as he clung onto his hard-fought position, but Hector's panicking horses carried him off together with the rest of the Trojan army, in frantic disordered retreat across the defensive ditch:

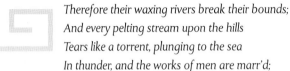

> *Therefore their waxing rivers break their bounds;*
> *And every pelting stream upon the hills*
> *Tears like a torrent, plunging to the sea*
> *In thunder, and the works of men are marr'd;*
> *So, with like thunder, fled the steeds of Troy.*

Behind the Trojans rushed Patroclus, urging the Greeks on through the clouds of dust thrown up by the fleeing horses. Charioteers were flung out and crushed underfoot as their teams swerved this way and that in wild panic. Achilles' extraordinary horses—a gift from the gods—served Patroclus well, taking him across the ditch in one single leap. It was Hector that he was after, but Hector's speeding horses had carried him out of reach.

With his rapid advance, Patroclus had cut off some powerful Lycian contingents, and leaving the pursuit of Hector he began to herd them back toward the killing grounds near the ships. Patroclus laid about him, slaughtering some of the leading Trojan warriors in revenge for the comrades he had lost. He slew Erylaus and Pronous and Erymas and Amphoterus. The hapless Thestor, hunched in his chariot having lost his mind in the terror of the rout, was speared through the face and hauled out of his chariot to die on the ground. When the Lycian commander Sarpedon saw how his men were suffering, he leaped down fully armed from his chariot, intending to deal with the mighty force that was driving his comrades in such confusion. Patroclus saw him and jumped from his own chariot, and the two rushed at each other.

In Olympus, Zeus was watching with pity, realizing that his son Sarpedon was about to be killed. In anguish he pondered whether to sweep him far away to Lycia and safety. But Hera admonished him, and told Zeus that he could not challenge fate. Sarpedon's destiny had been settled long ago, and if Zeus intervened in this way, the other gods would want to do the same for their children. So Zeus watched, powerless to stop the inevitable, sending down a shower of bloodlike rain as a tribute to his son.

As Zeus did this, Patroclus speared Sarpedon's attendant in the belly. Sarpedon flung his own spear, missing Patroclus but hitting one of his horses, which fell in the dust. But Patroclus' next throw was fatal. His spear struck Sarpedon in the chest and he crashed to the ground like a felled oak tree, calling with his last breath to his companion Glaucus, urging him to rally the Lycians and protect his corpse:

> *Come also, and do battle for my sake.*
> *For most of all to thee shall I become*
> *A byword everlasting and reproach,*
> *If ye should lose my body, and if the foe*
> *Thus in their galleys' midst should strip me fall'n;*
> *Therefore hold fast, and round me call the host.*

With these words Sarpedon gave up his spirit. Patroclus put his foot on Sarpedon's chest to draw out the fatal spear and his innards came out with the point. Glaucus heard Sarpedon's call with horror, but he was powerless to help, hampered as he was by the wound in his arm that Teucer's arrow had given him. All he could do was pray to Apollo to staunch his wound. Zeus had not even stirred to save his own son, but Glaucus would rally the Lycians to fight over the body of Sarpedon.

Apollo heard Glaucus' prayer, and he soothed the pain and dried the wound, filling him with renewed energy. Glaucus then called the Lycian troops together and urged them to greater efforts, before hurrying away to find the other Trojan leaders. He came to Hector and his other officers behind the lines and upbraided them for forgetting their allies, who were laying down their lives. Glaucus told them that Sarpedon was dead, and implored them to make a stand by his body.

Sarpedon had been one of the finest warriors in the entire army, and the Trojans were grief-stricken to hear about his death. Led by Hector, they dashed back into the battle to avenge him. At the same time, Patroclus was urging the Greek commanders to make an example of Sarpedon for being the first to storm the wall, by mangling his body and stripping its armor. As the two sides closed together into bitter fighting around the corpse, Zeus redoubled the slaughter by covering the battle in a veil of night.

At first the Trojans were able to force back the Greeks, but when Hector smashed the skull of one of the bravest of the Myrmidons with a rock, the enraged Patroclus raced through the front line in such a way that even Hector began to stagger back. As warriors swarmed like flies around Sarpedon's now unrecognizable body, the air resounded with the crash of metal on armor. But up on Olympus, Zeus was considering what to do with Patroclus.

Patroclus' fatal error

For the time being, Zeus allowed Patroclus to drive the Trojans back toward the city. He put a spirit of cowardice into Hector, who leaped into his chariot and called to the Trojans to escape while they could. This was too much, even for the Lycians, who fled from all that remained of the body of their lord Sarpedon, allowing the Greeks to strip the bronze armor from his corpse. Zeus then sent down Apollo to retrieve the corpse of his beloved son and take it back to his homeland.

Zeus was now inspiring Patroclus with reckless courage, so that he forgot the advice he had been given by Achilles and set off in pursuit of the Trojans and Lycians, even though he had been warned not to do so. His energy was such that he might have taken the city himself, were it not for Apollo's decision to make a stand under the Trojan tower. Three times, Patroclus scaled the wall of the city, and three times Apollo flung him down again. When he tried to return for a fourth attempt, Apollo shouted that the city was not destined to fall to him, but to a far better man. Finally Patroclus, realizing that he was contending with a god, retreated.

While Hector was waiting under the Scaean Gate, trying to decide the best course of action, Apollo came to him in disguise and whispered in his ear to urge him back into the battle to catch Patroclus. With the god behind him, Hector ordered his chariot back into the fighting, driving the horses onward toward Patroclus.

When the two warriors met, Patroclus flung a jagged rock which hit Hector's charioteer, his half-brother Cebriones, smashing his forehead and forcing his eyes out of their sockets and onto the ground. Patroclus mocked him:

Truly a nimble man! How well he dives!
So he were only on the pearly seas,
Plunging for oysters, large would be the haul,
Albeit the waves were rough, when he leap'd forth:
So perfect this nice dive from car to earth,
Such diving needs must be a trade in Troy!

Both warriors grabbed the body of the charioteer, Hector at its head and Patroclus at its feet, while the Trojans and Greeks rallied round them. Rocks and spears struck shields all around. As the sun started to dip below the horizon, the Greeks began to gain the upper hand. They captured the corpse of Cebriones and stripped off the armor. Then three times, Patroclus leaped at the Trojans, and created havoc, killing

27 men. But the fourth time—without realizing—he came face to face with Apollo, hidden in the midst of the battle, wrapped in a thick mist.

Moving behind Patroclus for a moment, Apollo hit him in the back, knocking his helmet off his head. It rolled away under the horses' hooves. Patroclus dropped his spear and it shattered on the ground, and the strap of his shield slipped from his shoulder. He was struck by a momentary blindness, which paralyzed him for a few seconds, and in that time a spear hit him between the shoulders, flung by Euphorbus, who dashed in and then slipped away. Patroclus retreated out of the battle to avoid his fate, but Hector saw he had been wounded and chased after him through the fighting, hunting him down relentlessly. Weakened by his wound, Patroclus could not resist, and Hector thrust his spear through Patroclus' belly, driving the weapon right through his body and out the other side.

Patroclus slumped to the ground. The Greek soldiers around him fell back appalled, while Hector goaded him as he lay there, gloating over his failure to make slaves of the Trojan women. Achilles might be the world's greatest warrior, but he was no help to Patroclus now. Patroclus groaned through his agony, saying that it was Zeus and Apollo who had caused his death, not Hector:

> *But Fate, fell Fate hath slain me; and of Gods*
> *Apollo, and of men Euphorbus, struck;*
> *Thine but the third part in my death. Yet hear*
> *These my last words, and lay them to thy heart:*
> *Nor thou hast long to live; but even now*
> *I see Death stand—Death and a violent Fate*
> *Beside thee; and the son of Aeacus,*
> *The blameless chief Achilles, strikes thee down!*

With these words Patroclus died, but Hector replied nonetheless, claiming proudly that Achilles might yet be vanquished by his spear:

> *Predoom'st thou me, Patroculus, to this death?*
> *Yet it may hap that Peleus' noble Son*
> *Shall be the first to perish by my spear.*

He placed his foot on Patroclus' chest, and drew out his weapon. Then he turned and set off in pursuit of Patroclus' chariot and the splendid horses of Achilles, but with Automedon at the reins, they were soon out of Hector's reach.

Book 17
STRUGGLING OVER THE BODY

Defending the body of Patroclus

Menelaus had seen Patroclus fall and rushed to protect his dead body, standing defensively over it with his mighty shield and spear. The Trojan Euphorbus, who had first crept up behind Patroclus and wounded him, was trying to claim Patroclus' armor as his rightful reward:

> *Chieftain Zeus-born, and leader of the host!*
> *Withdraw thee, quit the body, and permit*
> *To me the bloody trophy of those arms.*
> *None of all Troy nor Troy's renown'd allies*
> *Boasts to have struck Patroclus ere I struck;*
> *Suffer then that I take the fame I won*
> *Lest else thine own sweet life be also lost.*

Menelaus had killed Euphorbus' brother in the fighting, so Euphorbus had no reason to love him. He stabbed at Menelaus' shield with his spear, but the spear tip bent against the thick hide. At the same time, Menelaus threw the whole weight of his body behind his own spear and struck Euphorbus in the throat, drenching his golden curls in blood and leaving him lifeless on the ground. Menelaus set about stripping the body of its armor, and none of the Trojans dared to challenge him. Seeing this, Apollo devised a plan to stop him, and went to find Hector. Disguised as the warrior Mentes, he urged Hector to abandon the chase after the unstoppable divine war horses of Achilles, and go back to protect the body of Euphorbus. Looking through the battle, Hector saw what was happening and dashed at Menelaus, uttering a war cry that brought the Trojans with him, charging at his heels.

Menelaus and Great Ajax stood over Patroclus' body, protecting it from the ravages of the Trojans; they could not retrieve Achilles' armor, which Patroclus had been wearing, but they did save the corpse and took it back unmarked to the Greek camp.

MENELAUS

Menelaus was confused. If he abandoned the armor and the body of Patroclus, he would lose face among any Greeks that witnessed the scene, but if he stood firm and fought Hector, he was liable to be cut off from his own lines. Yet it would be madness to fight anyone who clearly had the gods on his side, as Hector had, and so reluctantly Menelaus retreated. When he reached the safety of his comrades, he sought out Great Ajax and urged him to hurry back with him to Patroclus. Hector had taken his armor, but they might at least save the body to bring back to Achilles.

Hector had stripped the armor from Patroclus' body and was now ready to haul it away, planning to cut off the head and give the trunk to the Trojan dogs. But in a moment Ajax was there, covering the body with his towerlike shield, and fending off the Trojans like a lion protecting its cubs. Menelaus was at his back with great misery in his heart. Hector quickly handed the beautiful armor to some comrades to take back to the city, and leaped into his chariot to retreat.

At once Glaucus challenged him, and condemned him as a coward. The Lycians had been fighting alongside Hector to defend the city, but with no thanks, and Hector had even abandoned Sarpedon's body to the Greeks. At a word from Glaucus, the Lycians would all withdraw now and leave Troy to its fate. If the Trojans could drag Patroclus' body into the city, the Greeks would immediately return Sarpedon's armor in exchange, but Hector was too cowardly to face Ajax.

Stung by this insult, Hector replied that he was not frightened of Ajax, but that Zeus ruled the battlefield and he could make even a brave man run away. Then he challenged Glaucus to stand alongside him and they would see who was the coward:

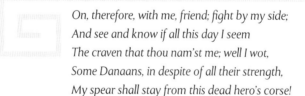

> *On, therefore, with me, friend; fight by my side;*
> *And see and know if all this day I seem*
> *The craven that thou nam'st me; well I wot,*
> *Some Danaans, in despite of all their strength,*
> *My spear shall stay from this dead hero's corse!*

With these words, Hector went off to catch those who were carrying the armor of Achilles that Patroclus had worn back to the city. He met them some way from the battle, and immediately he took off his own armor and changed into that of Achilles. From Olympus, Zeus saw what he was doing and shook his head sadly. Hector had no idea how close to death he was. He had been wrong to strip Achilles' divine armor from Patroclus' body. Zeus would allow Hector to be victorious for a while, but he would not let him escape the battle, and Andromache his wife would not receive the armor, nor ever see her husband alive again.

A struggle in darkness

GREAT AJAX

Wearing Achilles' armor filled Hector with savage energy. He sought out his closest allies, promising to share half the spoils with the warrior who could drag back Patroclus' body from under the protection of Ajax. Then the Trojans fell upon Great Ajax and Menelaus once more.

Although Ajax continued to see off the threat from the attackers and killed many of them, he began to fear that he and Menelaus would not escape from the battle, and that Patroclus' body would soon be food for Trojan birds and dogs. He told Menelaus to call up reinforcements from the Greek chieftains back at the ships. Menelaus uttered a piercing war cry, and first Little Ajax, the son of Oïleus, and then Idomeneus dashed forward to help protect the body. Hector, clad in Achilles' armor, continued to press home the Trojan assault against the Greeks' interlocking shields. On Olympus, Zeus was outraged at the idea of Patroclus' body becoming meat for the dogs, and sent down a mist to protect the Greek lines.

At first the Greeks were successfully pushed back, but as soon as the Trojans began dragging off the body, the Greeks were rallied by Great Ajax, who dashed through the fighting to strike Hippothous, one of the Trojan's Pelasgian allies, through his helmet just as he was tying Patroclus' foot to his sword belt. Hector hurled his spear at Ajax but he dodged it and soon it was the Trojans' turn to retreat. The god Apollo saw that they were in danger of being routed and came in disguise to Aeneas, upbraiding the Trojans for their cowardice. Aeneas recognized the voice of the god, and he shouted to Hector that Zeus was still on their side, and that they should not give up the struggle for Patroclus' corpse. Encouraged, Aeneas went into the front line and struck out savagely, but still the Trojans could not breach the defensive shields of the Greeks.

Ajax was organizing the Greeks well to defend each other and stay where they were next to the body. Darkness wrapped the struggle for Patroclus' body, but elsewhere on the battlefield the armies fought in clear daylight:

... no cloud was on the field
Nor on the mountains near; at ease they fought,
Each shunning oft the other's baleful dart
Or resting at safe distance. Other far
Their centre's plight, where round Patroclus' corse
Their chieftains in that darkness and close fray
Suffer'd most hardly, bruised by ruthless arms.

ACHILLES' HORSES

THE HORSES THAT
DREW ACHILLES IN HIS
CHARIOT WERE SO
EXTRAORDINARY THAT
IT WAS NO WONDER
THAT HECTOR CHASED
AFTER THEM FOR HIS
OWN. THEY WERE A
WEDDING PRESENT
TO ACHILLES' FATHER
PELEUS FROM
POSEIDON AND WERE
BOTH FAST AND
BEAUTIFUL BEYOND
ANY OTHERS ON THE
BATTLEFIELD. THEY
WERE ALSO VERY
SENSITIVE. WHEN
PATROCLUS WAS
KILLED, THEY WERE
CONSUMED WITH
GRIEF AND STOOD
WEEPING ON
THE EDGE OF THE
BATTLEFIELD.

The battle was now some way from the ships, and Achilles still had no idea that his friend and companion had been killed. He was expecting Patroclus to return after driving the Trojans past the Greek defenses. But Achilles' horses, given by the gods, knew all too well and were weeping for their temporary master, refusing either to go back to the ships or into the battle. They stood without moving and with their heads bowed, the tears running onto the ground and their beautiful manes soiled in the dust. There was nothing their new driver Automedon could do to persuade them to budge. Zeus looked down on the horses with pity and regretted that the gods had given them to mortal men who would die and let them share in their misery. Of all the creatures on earth, none were as miserable as men. But Zeus was determined that, although the Trojans would be allowed to advance to the Greek ships, Hector would not capture Achilles' sacred horses.

Zeus then filled the hearts of the horses with great courage and they galloped back into the battle. It was impossible for Automedon to control them and at the same time use his spear. Watching him struggle to control the horses, Hector realized there was an opportunity to capture them. He and Aeneas stepped forward with two companions to attack Automedon, but Zeus kept his promise and Hector's efforts were thwarted. The two Ajaxes came from the defense of Patroclus' body to assist, and Hector was forced to withdraw, leaving one of his comrades dead behind him.

Saving Patroclus

The fighting around Patroclus' body still raged fiercely, with defenders and attackers determined to die rather than yield. Zeus decided to send Athena to intervene again on the side of the Greeks and Menelaus prayed to her for the strength to fight for Patroclus. Delighted that Menelaus had prayed first to her, Athena emboldened him and filled him with courage. Apollo then in turn urged on Hector to avenge the deaths of those whom Ajax had killed. Hector marched forward in the glittering armor of Achilles, accompanied by a flash and a clap of thunder sent by Zeus to show that the tide had turned in favor of the Trojans. This was too much for the Greeks and some began to turn around to escape. Even Great Ajax began to realize that the situation was hopeless. Anyone could see that Zeus was on the Trojan side. Every spear they threw hit the target, while the Greek spears fell harmlessly to earth. And Menelaus couldn't even see through the murk, to find a messenger to take the awful news to Achilles; and he prayed to Zeus at least to lift the shroud of darkness:

> *But none can I distinguish, nought can see,*
> *In the thick mist that covers all the field.*
> *Save, from this darkness save, O Father Zeus!*
> *Give back the sky, and make our eyes to see;*
> *Grant light—destroy us after, as thou wilt!*

Zeus heard his prayer and cleared the mist and darkness from the battlefield, so that the sun burst through again. It was time to try to get a message through to Achilles, and Menelaus stepped back from the body reluctantly to find a messenger. As he left he implored the others to remember the gentle Patroclus and not to abandon him.

Menelaus went into the main battle and found Antilochus, and told him the dreadful news of the death of Patroclus and the capture of Achilles' armor. Antilochus was horrified, and ran from the battlefield in tears to alert Achilles. His mission accomplished, Menelaus returned to the defense of Patroclus. He knew that Achilles would not be able to come to the battle without his armor, and that they would have to come up with a plan to save the body and their own lives at the same time.

Only four defenders now remained by Patroclus' body. The two Ajaxes stood firm, keeping Hector and the Trojans occupied while Menelaus and Meriones carried the body of Patroclus back to the fleet. The Trojans roared with fury when they saw Patroclus' body being lifted up, but the two Ajaxes were too much for them. Menelaus and Meriones struggled back across the battlefield with their burden toward the black ships:

> *Nathless, like mules which ply a stubborn strength*
> *On a rough pathway, dragging down a steep hill*
> *Plank or hewn stem to be a vessel's mast;*
> *Though with the labour and the sweat their hearts*
> *Are faint within them, onward still they press;*
> *So with set hearts the two still bare their friend.*

Book 18
ACHILLES IN ANGUISH

Terrible news

INSTANT *ILIAD*

ACHILLES IS WORRIED
THAT HIS BELOVED
PATROCLUS HAS COME
TO HARM. WHEN
ANTILOCHUS
CONFIRMS HIS WORST
FEARS, ACHILLES IS MAD
WITH GRIEF. HECTOR
HAS HIS ARMOR SO HE
CANNOT FIGHT, BUT
NONETHELESS
ACHILLES GOES TO
THE FRINGES OF THE
BATTLE, TERRIFYING
THE TROJAN
ATTACKERS. UP ON
OLYMPUS, HIS MOTHER
THETIS ASKS
HEPHAESTUS TO MAKE
NEW ARMOR FOR
ACHILLES.

Achilles was watching the fighting with increasing alarm, especially when he saw the Greeks suddenly dashing in panic back toward the ships. He remembered his mother's prophecy: that the best of the Myrmidons would die, and Achilles would witness it. Then the messenger Antilochus rushed up to him with the news he had been dreading. With tears pouring down his cheeks, Antilochus reported Patroclus' death:

> *Son of the warrior Peleus! woe is me!*
> *Evil my tidings; would it had not been!*
> *Fall'n lies Patroclus; round his naked corse*
> *They battle now; and Hector hath the arms.*

Achilles was overwhelmed by grief. He picked up the dust from the ground in both hands and poured it over his head. He smeared it on his face and clothes. Then he lay on the ground, clawing at his hair, while his female slaves screamed and ran wildly around their stricken lord. Afraid that Achilles would slit his own throat, Antilochus grabbed his hands and held them tightly.

Achilles' mother, the sea nymph Thetis, heard his howls of anguish and gathered all the sea goddesses around her in sorrow, lamenting that she would never see her son come home again and that he suffered so much. She decided, though she knew she could do nothing to help him, to hurry to Achilles' side to find out what grieved him. One by one, the goddesses followed her up the beach to the Myrmidon ships, and Thetis begged her son to tell her the reason for his despair. After all, she reminded him, his prayers to Zeus had been answered: without his presence on the battlefield, the Greeks had suffered a serious reverse.

Thetis went to the smith god Hephaestus and begged him to make new armor for Achilles, because Hector had stolen his, having ripped it from the body of his friend Patroclus. Hephaestus agreed and made new greaves, body armor, a helmet, and a shield for the great warrior, all imbued with the power of the gods.

It is true, Achilles told his mother, Zeus had done what she had asked. But what did that matter now that Patroclus was dead?

But what delight to me in all of this,
When now Patroclus, my own dearest friend,
Hath perish'd? Him—him, whom of all my host
I honour'd most, loved as I love myself—
I have lost him! whom Hector hath slain, and stripp'd
Of all that wondrous terrible armour bright
Which Gods to Peleus gave, a glorious boon,
Then when they threw thee to a mortal's bed.

Now his mother's fate was to lose her son, Achilles said, because he had no wish to stay alive—except for as long as it took to take his revenge on Hector.

In tears, Thetis warned Achilles that the death of Hector would seal his own fate. Disturbed as he was, Achilles accepted the worst, bitterly regretting his idleness, his failure to protect Patroclus, and the rivalry and rage that Agamemnon had provoked in him. But there was now no choice, he said. The time had come to get out onto the battlefield, to embrace his own death, but to win glory in the time that remained to him. Achilles urged his mother not to keep him from the battle—there was no chance that he could be persuaded to stand aside.

Thetis accepted the inevitable, agreeing that Achilles should go forth and save his exhausted comrades from the Trojans, and from Hector who was now swaggering about the battlefield in her son's own armor. But she begged Achilles to wait before rejoining the battle, and promised to meet him at sunrise with another suit of armor from Hephaestus. Thetis sent her fellow sea goddesses away back into the deep, and set off for Olympus to ask the blacksmith of the gods for the most impressive suit of armor he had ever made. As she went, the nymphs disappeared into the waves.

The struggle for Patroclus

Meanwhile, the Greek warriors were streaming back toward their ships, and their shouts of fear at Hector's advance could be heard across the battlefield. It was almost beyond their strength to drag the body of Patroclus with them out of the way of the Trojan missiles. And Hector was not far behind, with his chariots and his infantry. Three times, he grabbed the feet of the body and began to drag it back; three times, the two Ajaxes managed to repulse him.

Hector was undaunted. He stood his ground, shouting his battle cry, and the Ajaxes were unable to drive him away from the remains of Patroclus. Hector would have succeeded in capturing the body had not Iris, the gods' messenger from Olympus, dashed down to urge Achilles to prepare for battle. Without telling Zeus or the other gods, Hera had sent her down to warn Achilles that the warriors were fighting over the body of his friend, and that Hector was set on cutting off Patroclus' head and sticking it on the palisade. Achilles must not at any cost allow Patroclus to become the plaything of the dogs of Troy.

Achilles asked Iris how he could go into battle without his armor. His own mother had forbidden him to fight without it and nobody else's armor would fit him. Iris replied that the mere sight of him, even without his armor, would terrify the Trojans and force them to break off the battle. Even that would give the exhausted Greeks a moment to breathe:

> Full well we know thine arms are with the foe.
> But moving to yon trench, ev'n as thou art,
> Show thyself merely; and the host of Troy
> For fear shall hold them from the fight, and so
> The Achaians in their toil may breathe again
> One moment—short the breathing-space of war.

Hearing these words, Achilles set off toward the battle, and Athena threw her aegis round his broad shoulders and crowned him with a golden cloud that flared above his head, and the light from it lit the skies like a beacon. Soon he had gone through the wall and taken his stand by the ditch, but—with his mother's warning at the forefront of his mind—he did not actually join the Greeks in the front line. Yet he stood and bellowed out his great war cry, and Athena echoed the shout across the battlefield.

Sure enough, the terrified Trojans were thrown into chaos. Even their horses could sense death and began to pull the chariots back around toward the city. Three times the voice of Achilles echoed over the battlefield, and three times panic gripped the Trojan lines. As many as twelve of their best fighters died there and then, entangled with their own chariots in the mêlée. With enormous

The mere sight of him, even without his armor, would terrify the Trojans.

relief, the Greeks finally pulled the body of Patroclus out of danger, and laid him on a funeral bier. His comrades gathered round it in tears, and Achilles joined them, horrified by the wounds on his friend's body. And behind them, the sun set.

After nightfall

HEPHAESTUS

HEPHAESTUS WAS THE SON OF HERA AND BORN LAME, WHICH SO DISTURBED HIS MOTHER THAT SHE FLUNG HIM IN DISGUST FROM OLYMPUS. WHEN HE RETURNED, HE WAS SO FORGIVING OF HER THAT THE GODS FLUNG HIM DOWN A SECOND TIME. BACK AMONG THEM, HE WAS THE CRAFTSMAN— BOTH INSPIRING CRAFTSMEN ON EARTH AND CREATING ALL THE PALACES ON OLYMPUS. MOST OF ALL, HE WAS REMEMBERED AS THE BLACKSMITH OF THE GODS WHO CREATED ACHILLES' NEW ARMOR.

The Trojans withdrew from the battle and gathered around to discuss their progress. They were too distracted by the sudden appearance of Achilles even to sit down to their evening meal. The great debater Polydamas, born on the same day as Hector, urged them to withdraw into the city. Now that Achilles had put aside his argument with Agamemnon, there was little chance that he would be content to keep the battle on the plain outside the town, but he would soon be targeting the Trojan women as well. Achilles would be out there in full armor in the morning, and then withdrawal would come too late. But if they thought ahead, the Trojans could be fully armed and ready to fight on the battlements.

Hector was angry with this speech, and complained that they had been shut up inside the city walls for far too long:

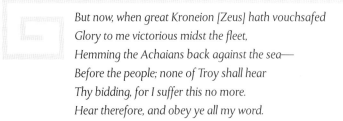

> But now, when great Kroneion [Zeus] hath vouchsafed
> Glory to me victorious midst the fleet,
> Hemming the Achaians back against the sea—
> Before the people; none of Troy shall hear
> Thy bidding, for I suffer this no more.
> Hear therefore, and obey ye all my word.

Hector ordered the Trojan soldiers to remain in the field and eat their evening meal in contingents. If Achilles really wanted to fight, then so much the worse for him, he said. The judgment and good sense of the Trojan warriors had been undermined by Athena, and they roared back their agreement instead of listening to the wise counsel of Polydamas.

On the Greek side of the battlefield, there was enormous grieving over Patroclus. Achilles laid his hands on his dead friend's chest and groaned aloud. He addressed the Myrmidons, bewailing the fate that was to redden the earth with his blood as well as his comrade's, and swearing not to bury Patroclus until he had brought back Hector's head. Achilles promised to slit the throats of a dozen Trojans at

Patroclus' funeral pyre. Then he told his companions to heat some water and wash the blood off the body, and to anoint it with olive oil and ointment. Patroclus' corpse was laid out in a linen cloth, and for the rest of the night the Myrmidons gathered around his body and mourned him.

The forge of Hephaestus

On Olympus, Zeus addressed Hera and acknowledged that she had achieved what she had wanted in bringing Achilles back to the battlefield. Hera was defiant, claiming that Zeus could not have expected her to do anything else in her anger against the Trojans. Meanwhile Thetis had come to Hephaestus' house. His wife, Charis, welcomed her in and called the lame blacksmith from his forge. Hephaestus was thrilled to hear that Thetis was visiting them, because the sea goddess had once rescued him after his mother, Hera, had flung him into the sea because of his disability. Quickly, he sponged the sweat off his skin, put on a tunic, and came to meet her. In tears, Thetis told Hephaestus what had happened to Achilles, and begged him to forge for Achilles a new suit of armor. Hephaestus told her he would do as she asked:

> *Be cheer'd, nor let this weigh upon thy heart:*
> *For would that in the coming hour of fate*
> *My power were such to hide him safe away*
> *From baleful death, as now to forge him arms,*
> *The marvel of the thousands who shall see!*

Hephaestus set to work straight away, urging his twenty bellows into life. He started fashioning a gigantic shield, with five layers of thickness, a rim of gleaming metal around the edge, and with a silver shoulder-strap. And all over the front, he decorated it with the most extraordinary pictures of the whole world, executed as only a god could. He embossed the metal on the glittering front with images of the sun, the moon, and all the constellations, and two towns full of people, with feasts and sieges and oxen and vineyards and dancing, and the ocean around the rim. After completing the shield, Hephaestus forged greaves and body armor and a mighty helmet with a crest of gold. And when Hephaestus had finished, he laid the armor before Achilles' mother. Thetis took it in her arms and swept like a falcon back down from Olympus to earth.

Book 19
ACHILLES TAKES UP ARMS

Achilles musters the Greeks

awn was breaking as Thetis came to the ships bringing the armor that Hephaestus had made for Achilles. She found her son stretched out on the ground, racked with long, heaving sobs, Patroclus' body in his arms. Around him stood a circle of mourning comrades. Thetis crouched down beside Achilles, slid her hand into his, and spoke softly to him. Achilles had to let Patroclus go and take up the magnificent gift that she had brought him:

> My child, despite our sorrow, yet awhile
> Suffer the dead to rest; and well thou know'st
> He had not fallen, except by hand of Gods;
> And take these glorious arms, Hephaestus' gift,
> Beauteous—no man hath ever borne the like.

Thetis laid the brilliant shining armor piece by piece on the ground. None of the Myrmidons could bear to look at such brightness, but Achilles did not flinch. He feasted his eyes on the glittering array. Gradually his grief was driven out by a stern joy as he looked at the gift his mother had brought him from the gods. Now he could go to war, but he could not bear to think of Patroclus' body rotting while he fought, worms seething within it, flies gorging on it. Thetis reassured him—she would infuse the body with ambrosia and nectar, food normally reserved for the gods, so that it would stay incorruptible until Achilles returned. Now he must muster the troops and arm for battle.

And so Achilles strode along at the edge of the sea, crying out to the Greek warriors. Everyone who heard him rose to follow, even those who were not there to fight, the sailors and helmsmen, the stewards, and quartermasters. They all made their way to the meeting place. At last their great hero was going to fight. Odysseus and Diomedes limped along as quickly as their wounds would allow, leaning on their spears, and sat down at the front. Last came King Agamemnon, his arm in a sling because of the heavy wound he had received from Coön.

The muster was complete. Achilles stood up to speak. He was brief, frank, and to the point; he realized that his quarrel with Agamemnon over a mere girl had simply made life easier for the Trojans, and accepted that the bitter pointless feud would be remembered by Greeks for years. But now was time to let the past go; he would renounce his anger against Agamemnon; now all he wanted was to destroy the Trojans:

At last Achilles deigned to fight, spurred on by the thirst for vengeance for his beloved Patroclus. His comrades were overjoyed because he was the greatest of all the Greek warriors and his presence on the field almost guaranteed victory and an end to war.

> *Yea, better had the dart of Artemis*
> *Slain her [Briseis] amongst the galleys on the day*
> *I took her, and Lyrnessus was despoil'd!*
> *So had been thousands saved their agonies,*
> *Who on the broad floor of the infinite earth—*
> *All for this anger's sake—have bit the dust;*
> *Sheer gain to Hector and to Troy; but long*
> *Shall Argos rue the strife betwixt us twain.*
> *Howbeit the past be past, whate'er its wrongs,*
> *All lesser pangs subdued in this extreme:*
> *I here renounce my wrath, and know my fault*
> *To nurse an endless anger. Therefore quick*
> *Arise, and wake to war Achaia's sons:*
> *That once again to meet the Trojans forth*
> *Advancing, I may try them, if they then*
> *Delight to take their rest so near our fleet!*

The cheering was deafening, as the soldiers demonstrated their joy and relief; their golden boy was back. Realizing that he had lost the initiative, Agamemnon, still seated on his throne, started grumbling about the noise and how a person could not hear himself think. He stood up and launched into a long speech. Where Achilles had accepted responsibility for his murderous rage and pride, Agamemnon insisted that whatever he had done, however much he was publicly reviled by his own troops, it was not his fault; Zeus and the gods had made him do it, although he acknowledged that it was up to him to make amends to Achilles:

ATE

WHEN AGAMEMNON
SPOKE OF SIN GUIDING
HIS ACTIONS, HE DID
NOT MEAN SIN IN
THE MODERN SENSE.
HE WAS REFERRING
TO THE KIND OF
DELUSION OR BLIND
FOLLY THAT FORCED
PEOPLE TO DO THINGS
THAT CAN ONLY END
IN DISASTER. THE
WORD FOR THIS IN
ANCIENT GREEK
WAS ATE; ATE WAS
CONSIDERED TO BE
THE ELDEST DAUGHTER
OF ZEUS. NO GOD OR
MORTAL WAS IMMUNE
FROM HER INFLUENCE;
WHEN SHE DECEIVED
ZEUS HIMSELF, HE
THREW HER OUT OF
OLYMPUS, AND FROM
THEN ON SHE COULD
ONLY WORK ON
MORTALS. SOME
TRANSLATORS GAVE
HER NAME AS RUIN.

Oft have I heard these murmurs of the host
Upbraiding—yet not I the cause, but Zeus,
Fate, and the Fury, shrouded all in mist:
These cast a spirit of wild Sin within me,
Then when I robb'd Achilles of his meed.
Yet what could I? Sin worketh through all life,
Sin, power divine, and ancient-born of Zeus,
All-wasting, all-destroying!

Even the Father of the Gods had succumbed to the wiles of Sin or Ate, his own daughter, Agamemnon went on, neatly bracketing himself with the all-powerful. When Zeus had boasted about the birth of his son Heracles, Hera had tricked him, and Zeus rued the day when he had been so boastful and overbearing. Now, in his turn, Agamemnon rued the day Ate had made him so high-handed in his dealings with Achilles. Zeus had stolen his wits and made him blind; but now he would make amends, and deliver all the prizes he had promised to Achilles. He could have the booty brought to the muster or sent to Achilles' tents.

Achilles, who had been champing at the bit, exploded with impatience. Why was the king fussing around about gifts and prizes when there were Trojans to be pulped? They were wasting time:

But now delight of battle be our thought!
Nor let us beguile the hours of war,
Nor linger here, our mighty task undone.
Soon shall Achilles once again be seen
Strewing with brazen lance the ranks of Troy;
Like him, let every Argive meet his foe!

Odysseus intervened quickly before Achilles and Agamemnon could talk themselves back into a feud. He did not want to see the fragile new order dissolve into anger and recalcitrance again, and offered conciliatory advice to both of them. Achilles should allow the men to go back to their ships and eat—Odysseus, the battlefield veteran, knew that an army marched on its stomach, and that men who were as brave as lions would be as weak as kittens if they were not fed. Agamemnon should bring the treasure to the muster, so everybody could see it, and publicly swear that he had never touched Briseis. Achilles should show some greatness of heart, and allow Agamemnon to give him a prebattle feast; and Agamemnon could try being as forgiving to others as he was to himself; there was no shame in making amends, even if you were the king:

> *Thou [Achilles] likewise, let thy heart be gentle in thee;*
> *And let him feast thee nobly in his tent;*
> *So shall the measure of thy claim be full.*
> *And thou, Atrides, learn from this time forth*
> *Justice, and know that princes, who offend*
> *Against who first offend them, have no blame.*

Agamemnon welcomed Odysseus' words, and ordered him to make the arrangements to bring the treasure; oaths would be sworn, and they should sacrifice a boar to Zeus, to make everything binding.

Achilles was pacing up and down seething with impatience by now; he could not believe what he was hearing. Couldn't they do this some other time? Hector was on top of them and all they talked about was their next meal. He wanted to drive into battle there and then, and save the feasting for a victory banquet. He could not eat, not while he still mourned Patroclus—his appetite wasn't for food, but for blood:

> *Still call I to Achaia's sons to move*
> *Forthwith to battle forth, nor break their fast*
> *Ere we have ample vengeance for our shame,*
> *But, after, sup victorious! Mine own self*
> *I vow, nor drink nor meat shall pass my throat*
> *Whilst he, my dearest slain, lies in my tent*
> *Still gash'd and seam'd, his feet toward the door,*
> *My comrades wailing round. I take no thought*
> *For mine own hunger or such cares at all;*
> *But slaughter only and the shedding of blood ...*

Odysseus pulled rank—Achilles might be the star warrior, but Odysseus was the survivor of many more campaigns. How could fighting men mourn their dead by starving themselves, when so many were dying, cut down by the will of Zeus? They could not afford such an indulgence, but must be tough, mourn for an hour, then get on with the fighting—and that meant eating to keep their strength up. Achilles had been skulking in his tent for too long—he had forgotten the brutal practicalities of war:

He could not eat, not while he still mourned Patroclus—his appetite wasn't for food, but for blood.

How can we mourn the dead by keeping fast?
Too many fall, too many, day by day,
One after other; grief would have no end.
No: hurry to their graves whoever fall;
Keep our hearts hard; or, maybe, weep one hour,
And then straight turn us to our drink and food,
Whoe'er hath come alive from out the fight,
So haply with more strength to meet the foe
Clad in unyielding mail to endless fray!

Then Odysseus briskly took charge, leading a squad to Agamemnon's tents to collect the booty, including Briseis.

After an age of bitter feuding, Agamemnon and Achilles were persuaded to come to a precarious understanding; Agamemnon returned the girl Briseis to Achilles, together with an immense amount of treasure. Oaths were sworn before either of them could change their minds.

Feast, fast, and oath-swearing

Agamemnon stood up. Beside him, the herald Talthybius held up the sacrificial boar, and Agamemnon cut tufts of bristles from its head, to set the ritual in motion. The army sat in silence while he held up his arms to pray to Zeus, and swore under oath that he had never touched Briseis:

> Thou first, O sovran Zeus, of Gods supreme;
> And Thou, O Earth; and Sun, I add thy name;
> And Furies, ye who deep beneath the earth
> Wreak the fell vengeance of an oath forsworn,
> Bear witness, that my hand hath ne'er been laid
> Upon this maiden, or for thought of love,
> Or any due of service; safe she dwelt
> Untouch'd within my tents. If this be false,
> May every woe be heap'd upon my head,
> Whate'er the Gods decree to man forsworn!

His blade flashed as he slashed the throat of the boar, and Talthybius hurled the animal into the sea, a feast for the fish. Achilles spoke in his turn; now he too blamed Zeus for what had happened. He was bitter, but brief:

> Vast of a truth the ills thou lay'st on man,
> O Father Zeus! How else would Atreus' Son
> Have stirr'd my heart thus to its deepest depths,
> And madly ta'en this maid in my despite?
> Nay; 'twas the work of Zeus, who will'd, perchance,
> Such death unto the many who have fallen.

Achilles dismissed the troops, ordering them to eat and prepare for war. His own Myrmidons eagerly seized the gifts from Agamemnon and took them back to Achilles' ships. So it was that Briseis came back to his tent—but when she saw Patroclus lying dead, she threw herself on top of him crying piteously. He had been so kind to her, even when Achilles had hacked down her own husband and three brothers before her eyes. Patroclus had promised that she should be saved, married to Achilles, and that he would organize the wedding party:

SACRIFICIAL TUFTS

AT EVERY SACRIFICE TO THE GODS DESCRIBED IN THE *ILIAD*, TUFTS OF WOOL OR HAIR WERE CUT FROM THE ANIMAL AND DISTRIBUTED AMONG THE CHIEFS. IT WAS IMPORTANT THAT SACRIFICIAL RITUALS WERE A COMMUNAL ACTIVITY, SO THAT ALL THE PARTICIPANTS HAD A STAKE IN THE PRAYER OR OATH. THE DISTRIBUTION OF WOOL AMONG THE CHIEFS MADE THEM A PART OF THE OATH-TAKING PROCESS. (SOME SCHOLARS SUGGEST THAT HOLDING THE HAIR OR WOOL CREATED A RITUAL CONNECTION BETWEEN THE VICTIM AND THE PARTICIPANTS, BUT THIS IS A CONTROVERSIAL ISSUE.)

NEOPTOLEMUS

NEOPTOLEMUS WAS THE SON OF ACHILLES AND DEIDAMIA, DAUGHTER OF THE KING OF SCYROS. ACHILLES HAD SPENT MOST OF HIS YOUTH AT SCYROS, DISGUISED AS A GIRL—THIS WAS PART OF HIS MOTHER'S UNSUCCESSFUL PLAN TO KEEP HIM AWAY FROM THE WAR. THE CHILD WAS NAMED PYRRHUS (RED-HAIRED), BUT IN THE *ILIAD*, ACHILLES CALLS HIM NEOPTOLEMUS, "YOUNG WARRIOR." AFTER HIS FATHER'S DEATH, NEOPTOLEMUS WAS BROUGHT TO TROY BY PHOENIX AND ODYSSEUS, WHO GAVE HIM HIS FATHER'S ARMOR. NEOPTOLEMUS FOUGHT WELL, AND WAS ONE OF THE WARRIORS IN THE TROJAN HORSE. HE SLEW PRIAM AND WAS GIVEN ANDROMACHE AS HIS PRIZE.

*Yet, though the fleetfoot hero so had slain
My husband, then despoiling Mynes' town,
Thou wouldst not suffer me to weep, but saidst
How thou would make me wedded wife, the wife
Ev'n of divine Achilles, bearing me
Home on his ships to Phthia, and wouldst feast
The Myrmidonians at our marriage there.
Wherefore for thee my tears shall ceaseless flow,
For thou wast ever gentle unto me.*

And she wept, and so did all the other women Agamemnon had given to Achilles. Briseis' grief stirred up Achilles' feelings once again. The Greek captains clustered round him, begging him to eat, to keep up his phenomenal strength. He would have none of it, he would fast until sunset, and he drove them away. Odysseus, Phoenix, Agamemnon, and Menelaus stayed and tried to lift his spirits, but memories of Patroclus came rushing back. There would be no comfort for Achilles until the heat of battle warmed his bereft heart. Achilles had always known he would die at Troy, but he had hoped that Patroclus would survive, to cheer the last days of Achilles' father Peleus, and to take his son Neoptolemus to see his father's fabulous wealth, and tell him stories of his achievements. Zeus took pity on Achilles and roused Athena, sending her to feed him nectar and ambrosia, so that at least when he fought, he would be strong.

Achilles rides out

Now it was time to fight. Warriors came pouring out of the ships and tents, tightly packed together like a great bronze snowdrift, the brightness of their armor lighting the skies. In the middle of it all, Achilles at last put on his magnificent armor and made ready for war. First he strapped the greaves onto his legs, fastening them with silver ankle clasps. Next, he tied the breastplate around his chest. Then he slung his sword in its baldric over his shoulder, the bronze-bladed sword with the silver-studded hilt. The great round shield shone like the full moon, flaring like a lighthouse beam as he swung it round and slid his arm through the straps. Last, he put on the heavy helmet, with the thick golden plumes dancing on the crest. Then he tested the armor, darting and spinning to see how it fitted. It was as light as air, sliding supple along his limbs, moving as he moved. Satisfied, he picked up the great ash spear that none could lift but him, a gift from his father. Automedon, his driver, brought his war chariot, and he stepped into it, the sun gleaming from his glorious armor. Achilles spoke to his immortal horses, Balius and Xanthus. They had to work harder this time and bring him home safe, not leave him dead on the battlefield as they had Patroclus.

Suddenly, Xanthus the stallion bowed his head; Hera had granted him the power to speak; but his words were not cheerful. They had been powerless to save Patroclus, because they were matched against Apollo; although they would bring Achilles home unscarred this time, soon they would be unable to help him.

> *Yet once again we bear thee scathless home,*
> *Our mighty lord Achilles; but the hour*
> *Of thy destruction draweth near; nor we*
> *The cause thereof, but Fate and Heaven most high.*
> *Nor to our sloth or speed inert impute*
> *That Troy hath spoil'd Patroclus of thine arms;*
> *For He, whom fair-hair'd Leto bare to Zeus,**
> *Best of Immortals, slew him in the van,*
> *Giving to Hector this renown withal.*
> *Swift as the blast of Zephyr, which they feign*
> *Swiftest of things created, we might fly;*
> *Yet may not save thee, who art doom'd to fall*
> *Slain by a mortal and a God combined.*
> **i.e. Apollo*

The horse was just as suddenly silent again, struck dumb by one of the Furies; but Achilles burst out angrily—even his horse was predicting a death he knew only too well was coming. The only thing left to him was to make the Trojans sick of war.

> *Thou too amongst the prophets of my death!*
> *But wherefore this, O Xanthus? For myself*
> *Know well my doom, that here I needs must die,*
> *Nor see my father dear or mother more:*
> *Not therefore will I slack me, or surcease*
> *Ere Troy hath own'd a surfeit of the war!*

With a blood-curdling battle cry, Achilles drove out to stand at the head of the army.

The great round shield shone like the full moon, flaring like a lighthouse beam.

Book 20
THE GODS AT WAR

The gods choose sides

INSTANT *ILIAD*

ZEUS CALLS A MUSTER OF ALL THE GODS, AND ORDERS THEM TO PICK SIDES AND FIGHT ALONGSIDE THE MORTALS. APOLLO SIDES WITH THE TROJANS, AND INCITES AENEAS TO CHALLENGE ACHILLES, WHO IS INVINCIBLE IN HIS GOD-MADE ARMOR. ALTHOUGH HE IS ON THE GREEKS' SIDE, POSEIDON STEPS IN AND SAVES THE TROJAN, WHO IS DESTINED TO SURVIVE. APOLLO PROTECTS HECTOR FROM ACHILLES' DEADLY SPEAR, AND THE GREEK CHAMPION, FRUSTRATED IN HIS MISSION, GOES ON A KILLING SPREE.

The Greeks formed up for battle around the glittering figure of Achilles, and faced the Trojan lines across the plain with hearts full of fresh hope and new purpose. Meanwhile, up on Olympus, Zeus ordered Themis to muster all the gods; every river god came, right down to the most negligible nymphs, all except for Ocean, whose waters hold the world together. When the gods had settled down in the great marble halls, Poseidon spoke up, demanding to know what his brother's plan was. Zeus replied that he was worried that Achilles in his huge anger would tear down the walls of Troy with his bare hands, against the decrees of Fate. Zeus was happy to let the mortals perish, but Fate's thread had to be followed. He commanded the gods to go down to the battlefield to fight with whichever side they chose; he would sit up on Olympus and watch, sending down judicious thunderbolts when he thought things were getting unbalanced:

> They perish, yet their doom is still my care.
> Here, sitting on this folded hill enthroned,
> Joying in sight of you will I remain;
> But ye go forth and each join either host,
> Each aiding either as his own heart bids;
> For, if Achilles fought with Troy alone,
> Then were no let at all to Peleus' Son,
> Before whose mere aspèct they quake for fear;
> Yea, in this fury for his comrade's sake
> I dread lest, baffling Fate, he takes the town.

Achilles and Automedon, his
chariot driver, finally took the
battlefield. After so long away
from battle, Achilles was
ravenous for blood, and
stormed into the enemy,
hacking and slashing at any
who stood in his path.

The gods lost no time in getting down to the battlefield. Hera, Athena, and Poseidon were all committed to the Greeks and were joined by Hermes and Hephaestus; Ares the god of war, Apollo, his sister Artemis, and mother Leto were for the Trojans, together with Aphrodite and Xanthus, the god of the mighty Trojan river, known by mortals as the Scamander.

Until the gods intervened, the Greeks were getting the better of it; Achilles, blazing with wrath and invincible in his god-given armor, raged like Ares himself; the very sight of him so sapped Trojan morale that their ranks were falling back fast. But that all changed once the immortals joined in the fight. Athena stood on the Greek rampart and bellowed her great battle cry; it was instantly answered from the towers of Troy by Ares, who blasted back with a great, booming whirlwind of noise, ripping up the battlefield, driving the Trojans forward.

So the gods breathed new battle lust into the mortals, driving the armies at each other again; but they were quickly distracted by the urge to settle old quarrels between themselves. When gods fought, the battle blazed with supernatural power; the world quaked and everything was louder and more terrifying. Zeus hurled down thunderbolts indiscriminately on both sides; Poseidon made the seas boil and the earth quiver. Mount Ida trembled from peak to foot, the walls of Troy shivered, and the Greek ships tied up along the beach danced on their moorings. Deep below, Hades, lord of the underworld, cowered under the onslaught, shrieking at his fellow gods, terrified that Poseidon his brother would split the earth right open and reveal all the loathsome rotting secrets of the dead.

Apollo, his golden arrows in his hand, challenged Poseidon; war-crazed Ares confronted wild-eyed Athena; Artemis, the huntress, squared up to Hera, the queen of spite; Leto took on Hermes; and Xanthus the river god tried to quench Hephaestus the god of fire.

Zeus with Agamemnon (left) and Menelaus (right). At this stage of the war, Zeus was evenhanded with his thunderbolts, but for much of the time he had been favoring the Trojans. This was a direct result of Agamemnon's disdainful treatment of Achilles; Zeus had promised Achilles' mother, Thetis, to restore his lost honor, and used Hector and the Trojans to batter the Greek forces until Agamemnon saw the folly of his ways.

Apollo and Aeneas

All the while, Achilles was burning to get at Hector; only the Trojan prince's blood could slake his thirst. Realizing this, Apollo decided on a diversionary tactic and, abandoning his fight with Poseidon, he flew across the battlefield to find Aeneas. Disguising himself as Lycaon, one of Priam's sons, Apollo called out to Aeneas, taunting him—what price now all those boasts Aeneas had made when they all sat drinking? Hadn't he boasted that he would face Achilles man to man?

Aeneas had an answer to this. He had already met Achilles in battle and he did not want to do it again; he had only been saved by the strength Zeus had given to him to run. Athena had been on Achilles' side, casting a bright clear light around him, making his aim unerring. No mortal could survive a one-on-one with Achilles—his spear always flew true, and there was always some god or other to intervene and save him. If the gods would even up the odds, though, then it would not be so easy for Achilles:

> Man therefore to Achilles needs must yield,
> By whom a God stands ever, shielding hurt;
> Whose dart withal, without such aid, flies straight
> Nor halteth, till it taste his foe's best blood.
> But, would some God draw even 'twixt us two
> The chance of battle's issue, then, albeit
> He boast him iron from head to foot,
> Yet easily he would not overcome.

Apollo egged him on. Why didn't Aeneas trust the gods? After all, he was the son of a goddess himself—Aphrodite was his mother—and she was a much more powerful being than Achilles' mother, Thetis, a mere sea nymph. Aeneas should not let Achilles' contemptuous boasting overpower him—he was better than the young Greek braggart. He should go and confront him, now. So, buoyed up by Apollo, Aeneas went through the lines to the front ranks, looking for Achilles.

Hera was horrified when she saw what was happening; she called Athena and Poseidon for a council of war. Apollo was backing Aeneas; they had to protect Achilles—they could make Aeneas turn back or one of them could go to Achilles, encourage him, reassure him that he was beloved of the best Olympian gods, that the gods on Troy's side were just windbags. Hadn't Zeus sent them all down to the

THE FATES

THREE FEMALE GODDESSES, EITHER THE DAUGHTERS OF NYX (NIGHT) OR OF ZEUS AND THEMIS, WHO, IN THE *ILIAD*, APPEARED TO DICTATE DESTINY. CLOTHO, THE SPINNER, SPUN THE THREAD OF BEING OF EVERY INDIVIDUAL; LACHESIS MEASURED IT OUT; AND ATROPOS CUT IT OFF. THE FATES WERE IMPLACABLE: IT APPEARED THAT NOT EVEN ZEUS COULD COUNTERMAND DESTINY, ONLY OBSERVE WHAT THE FATES HAD IN STORE BY PLACING EACH MAN'S FATE IN HIS GOLDEN SCALES. ONCE A FATE WAS WEIGHED, ZEUS HAD TO MAKE SURE THAT THE PREDICTED RESULT CAME ABOUT—ALTHOUGH HE COULD CHOOSE HOW IT DID SO. (EVEN HE COULD NOT SAVE HIS SON, THE TROJAN CAPTAIN SARPEDON, WHO WAS FATED TO DIE AT TROY.)

battlefield to make sure that Achilles did not fall at the hands of the Trojans? Achilles might panic if Apollo roared down on him, his true powers on full display:

> Yea, for what other cause made we descent
> All from Olympus hither, but to save
> Him [Achilles] from now suffering aught by Trojan hand?
> Enough, enough hereafter he must bear,
> All that upon his thread fell Fate hath spun
> From the first hour his mother gave him birth.
> But if no voice divine explain him this,
> He needs must fear before a god in arms;
> For Gods appal, appearing arm'd to men.

Hera fretted and panicked, but Poseidon remained cool. There was no need to worry—the Greeks were much stronger than the Trojans. They should leave the mortals to fight, and find a vantage point from which to watch the battle; but if Ares or Apollo started up with their tricks, then he and Hera and Athena would make them very sorry. So Poseidon led the goddesses to the great rampart built for Heracles when he was at Troy. At the same time, the Trojan gods, tiring of their immortal battles, gathered around Apollo on a hillside near the city, and settled down to plan tactics. Acutely aware that Zeus was watching them, neither side wanted to make the first move.

HERACLES' WALL

POSEIDON, HERA, AND ATHENA SAT DOWN ON A GREAT WALL BUILT IN TIMES PAST BY ATHENA HERSELF AND THE MEN OF TROY. IT WAS PUT UP AS A REFUGE FOR HERACLES, WHEN HE WAS TRYING TO SAVE HESIONE, THE DAUGHTER OF LAOMEDON, KING OF TROY, FROM A SEA MONSTER SENT BY POSEIDON. POSEIDON HAD SENT THE MONSTER TO PUNISH LAOMEDON, WHO HAD REFUSED TO PAY HIM FOR BUILDING THE CITY WALLS OF TROY.

Aeneas and Achilles

Down the strip of no-man's-land between the two armies marched the two mighty champions, Aeneas and Achilles, both itching for combat. Aeneas strode menacingly, rattling his bronze spear so hard that the crest on his helmet shook, but Achilles charged at him like a rampaging lion, a beast that has been once hurt and is looking for revenge, carrying his pain for Patroclus like the wound of a badly thrown spear.

They closed in on each other, each hefting their weapon. Achilles spoke first, taunting and sneering. Did Aeneas dare to challenge him? Why was he being so very brave? Was he hoping to win honor, maybe even the throne of Troy? Fat chance—not while Priam lived, sound in wind, limb, and mind, nor while his many sons stood in line.

Perhaps he had been promised a fine estate if he killed Achilles. Aeneas would find it hard work—did he not remember when Achilles had chased him down Mount Ida, and only Zeus had saved him? Well Zeus wasn't going to help him now:

> *... Thee alone*
> *Zeus and the other Powers of Heaven then saved,*
> *But shall not save thee now, albeit, I ween,*
> *Thou so revolv'st it in thine own fond heart.*
> *Rather I bid thee to thy ranks retire;*
> *Stand not persistent till the stroke hath fall'n;*
> *A fool learns wisdom, when a thing is done.*

Aeneas sighed loudly; Achilles' adolescent ranting did not worry him. Aeneas was not just any old Trojan—his mother was a goddess, as Achilles knew, and he could trace his ancestry back to Dardanus, founder of the royal house of Troy, and a favorite son of Zeus. Royal and divine blood flowed in his veins. But surely they weren't just going to stand around trading insults like fishwives in the midst of battle—he was ready to fight:

> *Wherefore what need to us of jeer and gibe,*
> *Each to revile the other, women-like,*
> *Who, anger'd with a spirit-wasting strife,*
> *Revile each other in the public way*
> *Things true or false, whate'er their anger bids?*
> *Thou wilt not fright me from my strength by words*
> *Ere I have made my venture—Haste then, haste,*
> *Be our spears quicker to the taste of blood!*

With these words Aeneas flung his spear at Achilles. The Greek warrior instantly thrust his shield out in front of him, away from his body, in case the point pierced through. But Hephaestus had made it five layers thick, a sandwich of bronze and tin with a heart of gold, and the spear point lodged in the shield. Achilles hurled his own spear, which tore through Aeneas' shield rim, its shaft just grazing his shoulder as it thudded into the ground behind him. Trembling—the spear had so nearly found its mark—Aeneas looked up to see Achilles hurtling wildly toward him, his sword flashing. Aeneas snatched up a huge boulder and was about to smash it down on Achilles; he did not know that the god-given armor would stave off the blow, allowing Achilles to finish him off.

Poseidon saw what was coming, and cried out to the other gods from his ringside seat. He felt sorry for Aeneas, who would surely die—he should not have listened to Apollo, who would not save him now. Aeneas had always offered gifts to the gods, so they should rescue him. Zeus would not thank them if they let him die:

> *Rather we pluck him from this evil doom,*
> *Lest Zeus withal be anger'd for his death.*
> *For well with Fate accords that he escape;*
> *Lest the great race of ancient Dardanus*
> *Be without seed and perish from the earth—*
> *Dardanus, most beloved of all the sons*
> *Of mortal women to Kroneion [Zeus] born.*
> *Long against Priam's race His wrath hath been;*
> *Wherefore Aeneas shall soon reign in Troy,*
> *He, and his children's children, to all time.*

He should not have listened to Apollo, who would not save him now.

Hera broke in on this Olympian hand-wringing; Poseidon could do what he liked, and she had nothing against Aeneas, but she and Athena had sworn solemn oaths not to lift a finger to help the Trojans. Taking this as tacit permission to intervene, Poseidon transported himself instantly through the battle to where Achilles and Aeneas were fighting. He cast a mist before Achilles' eyes, snatched his spear from Aeneas' shield, where it had lodged, and dropped it at the Greek hero's feet. Then he picked up Aeneas and propelled him far over the battlefield, over ranks of fighting men and charging chariots to a distant flank. When he had set Aeneas down, Poseidon gave him words of warning and advice. He could not take on Achilles and should not believe any god who told him he could; but once Achilles himself had been slain, Fate had decreed that no one would be able to kill Aeneas:

> *Aeneas, say, what God could bid thee stand*
> *Infatuate in arms 'gainst Peleus' son*
> *Stronger than thou, and favour'd more by Heav'n?*
> *Withdraw thee ever, when thou encounterest him;*
> *Else soon to Hades, though in Fate's despite,*
> *Before thine hour thou goest. But, when Death*
> *And Fate have ta'en Achilles to themselves,*
> *Then with good heart in the vanmost mayst thou range,*
> *O'er whom no other man hath power to slay.*

Leaving Aeneas dazed and confused, Poseidon rushed back to Achilles, still stumbling around in a god-induced fog, and cleared the mists away. Achilles glared about him. This was impossible—his spear lay at his feet, when he knew he had thrown it, and the man he had thrown it at had completely disappeared; he must have had a god on his side after all. Achilles decided to cut his losses and get back to less complicated fighting.

Achilles and Hector

A chilles leaped back into the ranks, urging everyone on—he couldn't do it all single-handed, but he would lead them, carving a path through the Trojans with fists and feet and brute strength, blazing a trail for them to follow. On the Trojan side, Hector encouraged his troops, telling them not to fear Achilles. Hector would take him on, he was not afraid of his fists of fire and iron strength. As one man, the Trojans raised their spears, ready for the charge, when Apollo suddenly appeared before Hector with an urgent warning:

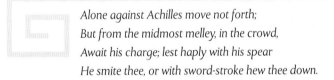

Alone against Achilles move not forth;
But from the midmost melley, in the crowd,
Await his charge; lest haply with his spear
He smite thee, or with sword-stroke hew thee down.

Hector was no coward, but the sight and sound of the god terrified him, and he took the advice and slid back into the ranks.

Not so Achilles; he flung himself upon the Trojans in a frenzy. His first kill was Iphition, who charged at him head on—Achilles split his skull in half, then roared as the still-warm body was cut to shreds under Greek chariot wheels. The fighting machine whirled on, spearing Demoleon, son of Antenor, through the cheek; the man's brains burst out of his skull, filling his helmet. Scarcely stopping, Achilles stabbed Hippodamus, who was fleeing from him; he fell bellowing like a sacrificial bull as Achilles' spear ran him through from the back.

Then Achilles saw Polydorus, Priam's youngest boy, whom Priam had forbidden to fight because he loved him so. But now the young hothead, intent on proving something, came pelting straight at Achilles; and Achilles took him down, spearing him through the neck so that the shaft came out through his belly, and he fell on his knees.

Seeing his brother tearing at his bowels in agony, Hector forgot Apollo's advice and charged dementedly at Achilles. Achilles was overjoyed—at last, the very man he wanted at the point of his spear; the engine of the Trojan army, the slayer of his beloved Patroclus, was rushing to meet him. He glowered at Hector, taunting, daring him to come nearer to meet his death.

Hector did not flinch—like Aeneas, he was not put off by sneers and gibes. Achilles was brave, and Hector knew that he was weaker, but it was in the lap of the gods. Hector hurled his spear with all his might, but Athena blew it back and it landed at his feet. Achilles, shrieking for revenge, ran at Hector, eager to cut him down; but suddenly Apollo appeared, wrapping Hector in a thick mist and whisking him away. Three times the furious Achilles thrust his spear into the clouds; the fourth time, he bellowed out in frustration:

> *Thou cur, who now again hast fled thy death!*
> *Ill press'd thee hard; but Phoebus yet once more*
> *Hath saved thee, unto whom thou needs must make*
> *Prayers endless, ere thou seek'st the clash of spears.*
> *Yet, let some God do battle on my side,*
> *Next when we meet, I ween I end thee quite ...*

They would fight again—next time the gods might be on Achilles' side. Meanwhile, the Trojan soldiers would pay dearly for Hector's defection. Achilles would now kill whoever he could reach.

Achilles, in his new god-crafted armor, a terrible blood-spattered sight on the battlefield, a killing machine whose reputation had gone before him; his presence, for so long a matter of fearful anticipation, was a huge psychological blow to the Trojans.

Achilles on the rampage

Raging like a berserker, Achilles surged through the Trojan ranks, dispatching Dryops with a spear through the throat, bringing down the strapping Demuchus with a crippling blow to the knee, then slicing open his chest. The two sons of Bias were skewered with a single spear thrust. One mad, desperate Trojan, Tros son of Alastor, tried to clasp Achilles' knees, to beg for his life: fool—even as the man pleaded with him, Achilles slit open his liver, leaving him to bleed to death in the dirt. Nothing could stop him—he sliced the top off Echeclus' head, then spitted Deucalion through the arm so that he could not move, but only stand helpless until Achilles lopped off his head and sent it flying, the marrow spurting up from the severed spine. Before the body reached the ground, Achilles was on to Rhigmus, whom he impaled and hauled out of his chariot as the driver was desperately trying to turn the horses; almost as an afterthought, Achilles dispatched the luckless charioteer, and the horses bolted in terror.

Like a god, Achilles blazed across the battlefield, untameable, uncontrollable, unstoppable. He plowed on through the Trojan ranks, relentless, like an ox crushing barley on a threshing floor. Blood swamped his chariot axle, and sprayed up from the churning wheel rims and the hooves of the stallions as they trampled over men, corpses, and battle shields. In the middle of it all, screaming with the exhilaration of destruction, rode the red-armed Achilles, sheathed in bright metal, and drenched with blood that was not his own.

CLASPING THE KNEES

THROUGHOUT THE *ILIAD*, GODS AND MORTALS WERE DESCRIBED AS CLASPING THE KNEES OF A MORE POWERFUL PERSON. THIS WAS THE RITUAL POSE OF THE SUPPLICANT, CROUCHING DOWN, ONE HAND CLASPING THE KNEE OR KNEES OF THE POTENTIAL BENEFACTOR, THE OTHER REACHING UP TOWARD THE CHIN. IT WAS A HUMBLING MOTION THAT SIGNALED A CONFESSION OF TOTAL POWERLESSNESS AND DEPENDENCE. IN ANCIENT GREECE, THIS SUBMISSION LAID A MORAL OBLIGATION AND PHYSICAL RESTRAINT ON THE PERSON BEING ASKED.

Book 21
ACHILLES AND THE RIVER

Achilles and Lycaon

Achilles charged on, the Trojan army fleeing before him, until they reached the banks of the fast-running Xanthus. There the panic-stricken mob divided—half of them ran for their lives, back across the plain they had crossed in triumph only the day before, following the mighty Hector. The rest of the army Achilles drove straight into the river, men and horses plunging together. They struggled and splashed and flailed and screamed, spinning helplessly on the whirling currents, the river roaring all around them.

Throwing his spear down on the bank, Achilles drew his sword and leaped down into the river, cutting and slashing until the water ran crimson. Trojans tried to get away from him, darting this way and that like shoals of small fish trying to outsmart a great dolphin. When his arm was tired from butchering, Achilles rounded up twelve young Trojans, dragging them soaked and dazed onto the riverbank, and tying their hands with straps cut from their own belts. Achilles had them taken back to the Greek ships, to become part of the blood price exacted for Patroclus. Then he stormed back to the river, his appetite for killing unappeased.

The first man he met was Lycaon, a son of Priam. Achilles recognized him instantly—the very man he had once captured and sold into slavery. Lycaon had hauled himself out of the river and was sprawled exhausted on the bank, his weapons strewn around him. Achilles could not believe his eyes. Here was a Trojan he thought he had dealt with ages ago, and now he was back again. This time he would dispatch him to his grave—no one could come back from there. Lycaon, seeing Achilles, got up and lurched toward him, arms outstretched to plead for his life. Achilles brandished his spear, but Lycaon came on, ducking underneath the shaft. He fell down before Achilles, grasped his knees, and begged for mercy. Did not Achilles know him? Had he not fetched a fine slave price? His true brother Polydorus had already fallen to Achilles—Lycaon was a son of Priam, but he did not share a mother with Hector:

> *Two sons she bare, and both will fall by thee;*
> *Already, ranging in the foremost ranks,*
> *One hast thou struck, the godlike Polydore;*
> *And now on me the selfsame evil falls.*
> *Fate brought me hither; scarce may I escape!*
> *Yet spare me, and remember this one thing;*
> *Not of that womb am I, whence Hector sprang,*
> *And Hector was the slayer of thy beloved.*

But there was to be no mercy. Lycaon's talk of ransom grated on Achilles' ears. Before Patroclus died, he had made a point of saving Trojan lives, sending them to slavery rather than death; not any more. Now, no Trojan was safe. Lycaon was going to die, and he would do well to stop whining about it. Patroclus, a far greater man, had died, and Achilles himself would die soon. Lycaon knew he was doomed; he gave up, sank back on his haunches, and offered himself up to Achilles, who immediately plunged his great sword into his neck. Seizing the body by one foot, Achilles hurled it into the river, taunting any listening Trojan:

> *Thither, to bed with the fishes, who shall lick*
> *The blood from off thy wound, without a care!*
> *But ne'er thy mother on thy couch shall lay*
> *Or mourn thee, but Scamander whirls thee out*
> *Into the broad-spread bosom of the sea.*
> *Yea, fattening on Lycaon's dainty flesh,*
> *The fish shall skim for joy the crispèd waves.*
> *So ye may perish, till we reach your walls,*
> *Ye fleeing, and I slaughtering in pursuit;*
> *Nor shall this smooth and silvery-eddying Stream*
> *Save you, albeit ye oft have offerings made*
> *Of bulls and living horses to his pools.*
> *Still, still, howe'er it please him, die ye on,*
> *Die evil deaths, till every man hath rued*
> *Patroclus, and that slaughter of the host*
> *Amongst the galleys, whilst I stood apart!*

Achilles leaped into the river to carry on his killing spree, hacking and slashing until the river itself cried out in protest.

But the louder Achilles boasted, the more angry Xanthus the river god became, and he began to think of ways to stop Achilles, and defend the men of Troy.

Xanthus rises

XANTHUS RIVER

ONE OF THE PRINCIPAL WATERWAYS OF TROY, THE RIVER WAS KNOWN TO MORTALS AS THE SCAMANDER. TO THE IMMORTALS IT WAS XANTHUS, THE NAME OF THE RIVER GOD WHO PRESIDED OVER IT. IT WAS WITH THE RIVER GOD, MANIFESTING HIMSELF AS TURBULENT WATERS, THAT ACHILLES FOUGHT.

Asteropaeus, the prince of the Paeonians, now stood waiting for Achilles with a spear in each hand, wet from the river but hot for vengeance for all the Trojans pitiless Achilles had hacked down in the water. Achilles was astounded. Who was this upstart? How dare he challenge the great Achilles? But Asteropaeus was no pushover—he hurled both spears at once and scored two direct hits. One struck the great shield but was stopped by the layer of gold at its heart; the other sliced across Achilles' arm, and drew blood. Achilles flung his spear in return and missed completely, the shaft sinking halfway into the riverbank behind Asteropaeus.

Achilles drew his sword and charged. Asteropaeus, now weaponless, tried vainly to pull Achilles' great spear out of the bank, to defend himself from its owner. Three times he tried, pulling as hard as he could, but it did not budge. Just as he was making a fourth effort, Achilles fell upon him, slicing his belly and spilling his guts. Asteropaeus fell to the ground and Achilles danced triumphantly on his chest as he stripped off the armor. Leaving Asteropaeus' mangled body as a feast for the eels and fishes, Achilles plucked his spear easily from the riverbank and turned his attention to the rest of the Paeonians. They began to run in terror seeing their finest cut down so easily, and Achilles' sword was a blur as he hacked them down one after the other—Thersolochus, Mydon, Astypylus, Mnesus, Thrasius, Aenius, Ophelestes. Finally Xanthus himself cried out in rage against Achilles—the river was being choked by the sheer number of dead bodies:

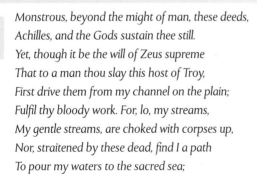

Monstrous, beyond the might of man, these deeds,
Achilles, and the Gods sustain thee still.
Yet, though it be the will of Zeus supreme
That to a man thou slay this host of Troy,
First drive them from my channel on the plain;
Fulfil thy bloody work. For, lo, my streams,
My gentle streams, are choked with corpses up,
Nor, straitened by these dead, find I a path
To pour my waters to the sacred sea;

And still thou spread'st around thee utter death.
Stay then thy hand; suffer their flight awhile;
Aghast I stand, dread hero, at thy work.

Achilles agreed to stop fighting in the river, but he declared that he would carry on killing until he had driven the Trojans back to their city and confronted Hector. Then he began laying about him again. Xanthus was not satisfied, and called on Apollo to help the Trojans:

Lord of the silver bow, and Child of Zeus!
Thou keep'st not well the counsels of thy Sire;
For strong on thee He laid the charge, to stand
Beside the Trojans, and sustain them still,
Till eve come shadowing all the fruitful earth.

When he heard this Achilles became even more enraged, and leaped into the torrent, ready to battle with the river itself.

Xanthus surged and boiled, throwing up onto the bank all the corpses that had been choking the flow; those still living were sheltered out of sight beneath the waves. The waters towered up over Achilles, then crashed down upon him, slamming against his shield; Achilles lost his footing, flinging his arms out to grab the trunk of an elm tree; as he clung to it, Xanthus tore at its roots, and it fell down, ripping away the whole bank. The tree fell across the river, making a temporary bridge, and Achilles quickly sprang across it to dry land. Xanthus surged along behind him, rearing up, a great black wall of water reaching for him like a dark claw. Achilles put his head down and ran for his life across the plain, but the water overtook him—gods are faster than mortals—and sucked the ground away from beneath his feet. As he struggled, Achilles cried out bitterly to Zeus; he was supposed to die nobly, at the hands of Apollo, not drown in a ditch like some ignorant farmboy:

O Zeus! on thee I call, great Sire, for, lo,
No God is near to pluck me (woe is me)
Safe from this death—oh, save me, and let come
Hereafter what come may! Nor blame of this
To other of Immortals, but to her
My mother, who with lying words beguiled
Her son, foretelling death hereafter doom'd,

To fall beneath the walls of armèd Troy,
Slain only by divine Apollo's shaft.
Liever than this had Hector struck me dead—
The noblest and the bravest of his race;
Then had a brave man slain as brave a foe.
But now behold me mesh'd within the net
Of vilest death, to perish overborne
By this strong stream, like any swineherd's boy,
Drown'd by a winter-torrent at a ford!

Hera and Hephaestus to the rescue

Zeus instantly sent down Poseidon and Athena, disguised as mortals; each took Achilles by the hand. Poseidon reassured him—it was not his fate to die like a drowning rat; he must push the Trojans back behind their walls and kill Hector, then go back to his ships. Athena was silently comforting, pouring her strength into the warrior's heart and limbs. The gods dissolved away in a mist, and Achilles ran on, reinvigorated. The river had flooded the plain completely; it was awash with dead men, body parts, and abandoned armor. Achilles shouldered the waters aside, wading through the floating corpses with high-stepping strides, and the river could not stop him, for all its powerful tide, because Athena had made him strong. So Xanthus called on his brother Simois to help him stop Achilles from smashing down the walls of Troy:

... Then I ween
Not all his might nor beauty, nor yon arms
Resplendent shall avail him; low in slime
Engulf'd beneath our waters those bright arms
Shall lie; himself in sands I swathe far-sunk;
And silt and rock full many a fathom deep
Showering, I fold him in such stony shroud,
Ne'er shall his people gather up his bones;
But there the pillar of my rocks shall rise,
That, when the Achaians gave him funeral due,
They shall not need the toil to pile his cairn.

Achilles shouldered the waters aside, wading through the floating corpses.

Xanthus rose once more, a huge crimson-crested wave of foam and blood and dead men. He would have swept Achilles away but Hera saw what was happening and dispatched her son Hephaestus, the fire god, down to help. Burning with bright, unquenchable, divine fire, Hephaestus swept down upon the flooded plain; Hera conjured up a drying wind and together they burned the bodies and boiled away the water, leaving the plain parched. Turning to Xanthus, Hephaestus incinerated the reeds and trees that lined the banks, and wrapped the river in a ball of flames, burning so fiercely that the fishes and eels boiled alive and the river was scalded. Xanthus cried out for mercy, in a voice that spat and snarled like the flames crackling under a cauldron of overheated fat; he begged Hera to call her son off:

> Wherefore, O Herè, bidd'st thy son assail
> Me only to such torment? Not to me
> So large the blame, as to the other Powers
> Who war for Troy. But, if thou so desire,
> I war no longer. Let him likewise cease;
> And I will swear never again to move
> For Ilion, not though all her roofs should blaze,
> Enkindled by Achaia's conquering sons.

Triumphant, Hera ordered her son to stop, and the river retreated to its proper bed.

However, the fighting between Hephaestus and Xanthus triggered the other gods into action, and they started fighting among themselves. The earth roared, and the heavens resounded with the noise as they clashed, and Zeus rubbed his hands in glee—he loved to see them fighting. Ares, predictably, led off, charging at Athena, screaming insults; he had not forgiven her for setting Diomedes against him, and driving the Greek's spear into him herself. With his giant lance, he struck the great battle shield she carried. Athena backed off, picked up a huge, jagged boundary stone, and hurled it at Ares, hitting him on the neck and sending him sprawling; as he lay there, she taunted him:

> Fool! Hadst thou erst not knowledge of my might,
> How far beyond thine own, that thus thou daredst
> To set thyself against me? This hath fall'n,
> The vengeance by the Furies for the sake
> Of thine own mother now of thee required,
> Whose wrath is heavy upon thee, for that thou
> Hast left the Achaians, and hast holpen Troy!

As the great brute lay groaning on the ground, Aphrodite rushed to help him, taking his hand to lead him away from the fighting. But Hera saw her, and called to Athena to go after her. Athena pounced joyfully onto Aphrodite, pummeling her breast with her fists. Aphrodite collapsed next to Ares, both gods helpless under Athena's assault. She crowed her victory—anybody else who supported Troy would get the same treatment:

> And like to these be whosoe'er for Troy
> Battle against Achaia's mailèd might;
> So strong in all endeavour, high in heart,
> As Aphroditè, when to Ares' help
> She came, and dared encounter of my spear!
> So had we long since spoil'd the stately towers
> Of Ilion, and for ever stay'd the war.

Poseidon and Apollo meanwhile agreed not to fight. Poseidon reminded Apollo that they had once worked together as slaves to build the walls of Troy and had both been betrayed by Laomedon. It was surely not worth fighting over the fate of his sons. Apollo agreed—he did not want to fight his own uncle, and certainly not for the sake of mortals, whose lives were just leaves in the wind. But Artemis, Apollo's sister, burst in; she was disgusted with her brother and reproached him for handing victory over to Poseidon so meekly:

> Fleest thou, O Bender of the silver bow?
> Fleest thou, and to Poseidon all the fame
> Surrenderest of a triumph unwithstood,
> Won without fight? Oh, what avails the bow
> Vain-dangling from thy shoulder? Ne'er again
> Dare in my hearing at the feasts of Zeus
> Thine olden boast, how once before the eyes
> Of all the heavenly host thou daredst oppose
> In single fight, Poseidon, hand to hand!

Apollo ignored her, but Hera flew into a rage. How dare Artemis challenge her—she should stick to what she knew, hunting down mountain deer, and not tangle with a higher goddess. With that, Hera tore Artemis' bow and quiver from her, and boxed her around the ears with her own weapons. Arrows flew all over the place, and

ARTEMIS

The Trojan forces stampeded into the city, parched, dustblind, and terrified.

Artemis burst into tears and stumbled away feeling sorry for herself. She fled to Olympus, to Zeus, where she climbed into his lap like a little girl and sobbed into his beard. When he asked who had committed this foul outrage, she immediately blamed Hera; and Zeus chuckled.

Achilles at the gates

Gradually, the other gods drifted back to Olympus, either triumphant or sullen. Only Apollo remained below, and he went to Troy. He was afraid that the Greeks might tear down the walls of Troy that very day, which was not part of Destiny's plan. Achilles, free of the river, had been relentlessly hacking a blood-spattered path to the city.

Priam stood on Troy's topmost tower, tracking Achilles' progress, watching in despair as the Trojans fled back in disarray. He ordered the gates to be opened, so that the soldiers could get in quickly. Priam knew that they were all in for a terrible drubbing—he was afraid that Achilles would simply burst through the walls. The Trojan forces stampeded into the city, parched, dustblind, and terrified, with Achilles snapping at their heels, shaking his great spear in frenzy.

The Greeks would have taken the city there and then, but Apollo inspired Agenor, son of Antenor, to make a stand against Achilles. Agenor stood stock still outside the city gates, but in his mind was a furious debate—what should he do? If he ran, Achilles could run faster and catch him, spearing him down in ignominy. On the other hand,

although Achilles was too strong for any man on earth, he was mortal. His power was only borrowed from Zeus—he might still have a chink in his armor. Agenor made his decision. He sprang out like a wounded leopard, ready to triumph or go down fighting. Holding his shield in front of him, he aimed his spear, and shouted out a last desperate challenge—Achilles need not think that Troy would fall undefended:

The routed Trojan forces, hearts, minds, and limbs bedazzled by the terrible Achilles, were driven back to the walls of their own city, fighting all the way; all those who had died getting them to the Greek ships were sacrificed in vain.

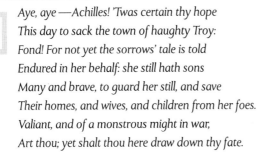

> *Aye, aye —Achilles! 'Twas certain thy hope*
> *This day to sack the town of haughty Troy:*
> *Fond! For not yet the sorrows' tale is told*
> *Endured in her behalf: she still hath sons*
> *Many and brave, to guard her still, and save*
> *Their homes, and wives, and children from her foes.*
> *Valiant, and of a monstrous might in war,*
> *Art thou; yet shalt thou here draw down thy fate.*

Agenor hurled his spear. It hit Achilles on the shin, but bounced off, foiled by the god-made armor. The attack shocked Achilles, though, and he sprang on the Trojan—but Apollo had a trick up his godly sleeve. Wrapping the real Agenor in a mist, he spirited him away to safety, then stood in front of Achilles disguised as Agenor, taunting him. Achilles chased after the god, and Apollo led him a merry dance, weaving and doubling back over the wheatfields, then running toward the river. Apollo stopped every now and then to let Achilles almost catch up, and so lured him farther and farther away from Troy. The rest of the Trojans, those whose legs could still carry them, staggered into the safety of the city.

Book 22
THE DEATH OF HECTOR

Achilles returns to the gates

The Trojans sank back, panting and exhausted inside the battlements, at last able to rest and satisfy their thirst. The Greek army, meanwhile, advanced right up to the city wall. Apollo then decided to reveal his trickery to the furious Achilles:

> Wherefore, Achilles, this thy vain pursuit,
> For thou art mortal, I a heavenly God?
> Is't that thou yet not know'st me for a God,
> That thus a quenchless fury drives thee on?
> Or that the routed Trojans' safe escape
> Into Troy-wall, whilst thou art wandering here,
> Is now no more thy trouble? Yet beware:
> Fate cannot touch me; me thou wilt not slay.

Achilles was disgusted at the deception, bitterly regretting the Trojans who would by then have been lying dead if he had not been lured away. He promised Apollo that if he had the power he would certainly have taken revenge. Then Achilles dashed back, running effortlessly, toward the city.

The first to see him in the distance, with the bronze shining on his chest like a star, was old King Priam. He groaned with despair and beat his head against the wall and shouted down from the battlements to his son, Hector, still standing implacably in front of the gates. Priam warned Hector that Achilles was far stronger than him: he had already killed two of Priam's sons. If Hector fought Achilles alone he would simply throw his life away, just when the city needed his protection. If Hector was killed, said Priam, his own death could not be far away:

Achilles and Hector finally met and fought; the climactic event that the whole poem had been leading up to. Achilles could not wait to fight Hector, even though he knew that it was his fate to die soon after he had killed the defender of Troy.

THE DARDANIAN GATE

ALONG WITH THE
SCAEAN GATE, THE
DARDANIAN GATE WAS
ONE OF THE MAIN
EXITS AND ENTRIES
TO THE CITY OF TROY,
AND THE GATE
THROUGH WHICH
HECTOR TRIED TO
ESCAPE FROM ACHILLES.
THE DARDANIANS, LED
BY AENEAS, WERE
RELATED TO THE
TROJAN ROYAL LINE.
DARDANUS HIMSELF
HAD BEEN THE SON OF
ZEUS AND ELECTRA,
ONE OF THE PLEIADES,
BUT HIS DESCENDANTS
WERE DIVIDED IN TWO
SOME GENERATIONS
BEFORE, AND THE
DARDANIANS NOW
LIVED UNDERNEATH
MOUNT IDA.

And dogs— the door-hounds at my table fed,
Oft with my own hands tended in the house—
Will rend me in their ravin, carrion-like,
Lap up my blood, and bask before my gates!
Such death—to lie thus gash'd and seam'd with wounds—
Well fits the warrior falling in his prime;
For whatsoe'er be shown, youth is not shamed.
But when an old man falls, and dogs may wreak
On hoary head and hoary chin and all
The exposèd limbs of age their own foul wills,
Nought is more piteous in this piteous world.

But neither his father's or mother's pleas would shake Hector's determination. He stood firm waiting for Achilles, but his inner thoughts betrayed some indecision. He remembered the ridicule he had heaped on Polydamas the night before when Polydamas had urged his fellow Trojans to retreat behind the walls. If only he had taken that advice. His arrogance then had come close to destroying the army, and his comrades would say it might now be better for him to die gloriously in front of the city.

Hector wondered what terms Achilles might accept—whether he should offer to return everything Paris had stolen and hand over the wealth of Troy—but he realized there was no chance that Achilles would consider such a proposal. If Hector so much as broached the idea to Achilles, he would cut him down without pity or respect:

... Ah, but tush!—
Why doth my dear mind thus discourse to me?
Not so may I approach him: neither grace
Nor mercy would he show, but slay me there
As helpless as a girl, without mine arms.
No gentle tryst can our encounter be ...

But when Hector saw Achilles approaching, he lost his nerve. First he began to tremble, and then he fled, and Achilles set off in pursuit. Some way out from the city, the two ran along the wagon road, past the twin streams—one boiling hot and the other freezing cold—where the Trojan women used to wash their clothes in the days of peace. Soon they had gone the whole way around the city walls, and were starting their second circuit. Three times Hector ran at full speed around Troy, with Achilles behind him.

Athena intervenes

On Mount Olympus, Zeus was looking down sadly on this sight; he was uncharacteristically sympathetic to Hector's plight, just as he had been to that of his son Sarpedon. He asked the other gods to help him decide whether they should save Hector's life:

> *Shame on me, who behold a man so dear*
> *Thus hunted round Troy-wall: my heart pleads loud*
> *For Hector, who hath oft, off Ida's peaks,*
> *Or from his city's topmost pinnacle,*
> *Made me burnt-offerings of the fat of bulls;*
> *Whom now with swiftest foot his heaven-sprung foe*
> *Hath thrice round Priam's palaces pursued.*

But Athena challenged him briskly, saying that he could not thwart the decrees of Destiny. Seeing that she was determined to act, Zeus gave his permission, and Athena dashed down to the battlefield. Hector was trying to reach the Dardanian gate, in the hope that he could get close enough to the wall for the warriors on the battlements to protect him with their missiles. But each time he drew near, Achilles moved closer to the walls and was able to head him off. Apollo gave Hector a final burst of speed so that he could stay out of reach, but at length Zeus took up his golden scales and placed a fate in each pan for the two warriors. The scale containing Hector's fate fell, and then even Apollo deserted him.

Athena came to Achilles and told him to stay where he was while she persuaded Hector to stand and fight:

> *O thou, the star of men and loved of Zeus!*
> *Soon shall we two achieve a noble name,*
> *Here in the face of all Achaia's host,*
> *On Hector, sateless though he be of war;*
> *For whom no manner of refuge now remains;*
> *Not though Apollo grovel on the floor*
> *Beseeching at the feet of Father Zeus.*
> *Stand therefore thou, and breathe thee; I depart,*
> *And tempt him to assail thee, might to might.*

Achilles paused and leaned on his mighty spear in order to regain his breath. Then, disguised as his brother Deiphobus, Athena walked right up to Hector, and promised to stand at his side so that they could take on Achilles together. Enormously relieved and grateful, Hector thanked Deiphobus for being the only one to risk coming out of the city. Then, believing that Deiphobus was at his side, Hector stepped forward to fight.

When the two warriors came within earshot, Hector promised not to run any further but to stand and fight. He asked for an agreement between them that whoever won the battle would strip the armor from their opponent's body, but would then hand it back to the other side for a proper funeral. But Achilles would have none of it:

> *Speak not of pact to me, thou hound accursed!*
> *As men to lions, or as wolves to lambs,*
> *So I to thee; and as twixt these and those*
> *Peace can be never, but unending hate,*
> *So thou and I can never be as friends.*

Achilles warned Hector that there would be no escape for him. And with that he flung his enormous bronze spear. Hector ducked and the spear flew over his head and plunged into the ground. Hector goaded his enemy for his glib tongue and premature threats, but he failed to notice that Athena had crept around and picked up Achilles' spear and handed it back to him.

Offering his own prayers, Hector then threw his mighty spear, urging it on toward its mark. It struck the very center of Achilles' shield and bounced harmlessly away. Hector was dismayed that his attack had failed, and called out to Deiphobus to hand him another spear. Turning around to look for his brother, Hector realized that he had been tricked:

> *Clear, clear the Gods now call me to my death.*
> *To mine own heart I said, Deiphobus*
> *Stands by me, but behold within the walls*
> *He bides, and Pallas hath beguiled mine eyes.*
> *Now death, fell death is on me, close at hand:*
> *Nor hope of refuge left; for though they oft*
> *Erewhiles befriending saved me, yet this doom*
> *Was aye the issue dearer from old time*
> *Ee'n to Zeus' self, and Zeus' far-smiting Son.*

The revenge of Achilles

Hector collected himself, realizing that there was still time to win glory so that future generations would remember how he died. He drew his sword and swooped like an eagle onto Achilles, who leaped forward to meet him with his spear in his hand. The point glittered as he sought out the most vulnerable spot on Hector's body, the unarmored flesh at his throat.

As Hector lunged at him, Achilles drove his spear into this spot. The spear went right through Hector's neck, and the Trojan collapsed in the dust. Achilles crowed triumphantly over his dying body, jeering at him for believing himself safe when he stripped the armor from Patroclus' body. He reminded Hector grimly that his body was to be thrown to the dogs.

Hector begged Achilles to ransom his body so that it could be taken home and cremated properly. But Achilles refused. There was no price he would be willing to accept in return for the body. In fact, if he could bring himself to do it, he was prepared to carve Hector up and eat him raw in revenge for what he had done. With his last breath, Hector warned Achilles of his own fate:

> *Yea, knowing thee, this also I foreknew,*
> *I might not turn thee; iron is thy heart.*
> *Yet take thou heed, lest I become to thee*
> *Cause of the Gods' just anger, on the day*
> *When Paris and Apollo lay thee low,*
> *Maugre thy valour, in the Scaean gates.*

Achilles spat back that he would welcome his own death when it came. But it was too late. Hector was dead.

DEIPHOBUS

WHEN ATHENA WANTED TO TRICK HECTOR INTO STANDING FIRM AGAINST ACHILLES, SHE PRETENDED SHE WAS HIS BROTHER DEIPHOBUS. ALTHOUGH HECTOR HAD MANY BROTHERS—HIS FATHER PRIAM HAD NEARLY 50 SONS—DEIPHOBUS WAS ONE OF THE MOST RELIABLE WARRIORS AMONG THEM. AFTER THE DEATH OF PARIS, HE WAS DESTINED TO MARRY HELEN. HE WAS ALSO DESTINED TO BE KILLED BY MENELAUS DURING THE SACK OF TROY.

Hector's mother screamed and his father groaned, and the cry of despair echoed all over the city.

The mourning of Troy

A chilles pulled his spear out of the body and removed Hector's blood-stained armor. As he did so, other Greeks dashed over and gazed down at Hector's handsome face and figure. As they went past, each one stabbed a weapon into the body, joking crudely that Hector was much easier to handle now than when he was setting fire to their ships.

Achilles urged his comrades to circle the city walls to see if the Trojans might surrender now that Hector was dead. Then he remembered Patroclus, still unburied back at the ships. He pierced Hector's ankles, threaded leather straps through them, and attached them to the back of his chariot. He lashed his horses into action, dragging Hector's body behind him, his head bumping on the ground, and his dark hair streaming out in the dust.

Watching the dreadful scene from the city walls, Hector's mother screamed and his father groaned, and the cry of despair echoed all over the city. The Trojans physically had to prevent Priam from going outside to beg Achilles for Hector's body. The king lay down in the dung by the city gate bitterly lamenting his loss.

Hector's wife Andromache had not heard the news, and had no idea that her husband was even outside the gates. She had been busy preparing a hot bath for his return. But she began to hear the noise of grief, and picked out the sound of Hector's mother, leading the lamentation. Dashing out of the house, fearing the worst, she reached the tower. In the distance, she could see her husband's body being dragged away toward the Greek ships. She fainted, falling backward onto the ground.

Killing Hector was not enough for Achilles; in his raging grief for Patroclus he wanted to punish him even after death, and so lashed the body to his chariot by the heels, and dragged it back through the dust to the Greek camp, bringing despair to Trojans, watching powerless from their city walls.

Her sisters-in-law gathered around to support her as she came around. She cried out in terrible distress; Hector, her beloved husband was gone, leaving her to lonely widowhood; she wished she had not been born to suffer this. But most of her woe was for her infant son Astyanax, adored by the father who would never see him grow up. Even if he survived the war, he would lead a miserable life, orphaned and alone, without his lands or his friends, reduced to patronizing hand-outs or, worse, rejected by those who had once honored his father. Once he had slept in a soft bed and enjoyed good things of life; but now he would be thrust into a life of poverty and neglect. His name, Astyanax, meant "prince of the city," but the city had stood only because of Hector's protection, and now he was gone. Heartbroken, Andromache vowed that she would make a funeral pyre of his clothes, since she could not have his body:

> *... for by thee alone,*
> *O Hector, stood these battlements and towers!*
> *Yet soon, amid the enemy's fleet, and far*
> *From father and from mother, writhing worms*
> *Shall of thy flesh eat all the dogs shall spare,*
> *There where thou liest uncover'd to the winds;*
> *Whose raiment, rich and delicate, and spun*
> *By hands of women, in thy home remains.*
> *This will I burn upon a blazing pyre;*
> *Not that it can avail thee, when thyself*
> *Art lacking, but that honour may be done*
> *To thee by all thy country o'er the tomb!*

Book 23
THE FUNERAL
OF PATROCLUS

Funeral preparations

Returning from the battlefield, the Greek soldiers dispersed to their ships. But the Myrmidons gathered around Achilles, who urged his companions to keep their horses in harness and to drive their chariots around the body of the dead Patroclus in honor of him:

> *O famed for swiftest steeds, my countrymen,*
> *My comrades proved and loved! Unyoke not yet*
> *Our horses; but with horses and with cars*
> *Move we around Patroclus, making wail*
> *And dirge—the honours due unto the dead.*
> *But when our souls are satisfied of wail,*
> *Loose then the steeds, and here we take repast.*

Weeping bitterly, Achilles and the Myrmidons circled the corpse of Patroclus three times in their chariots. Achilles addressed his dead friend, saying that he had dragged Hector's body back to feed raw to the dogs and promising again to cut the throats of twelve Trojans at Patroclus' funeral pyre. He flung Hector's body down in the dust next to Patroclus, while his warriors took off their armor, unhitched their horses, and sat down by Achilles' ship. Oxen, goats, sheep, and pigs were slaughtered ready for the funeral feast, and were laid to cook across the flames.

While these preparations were taking place, Achilles was led unwillingly by the other Greek leaders to see Agamemnon. Outside Agamemnon's tent, they set up a giant cauldron over the fire, hoping to persuade Achilles to wash the dried blood off his body. But Achilles refused and swore by Zeus not to let water near him until he had cremated Patroclus. He demanded that Agamemnon organize search parties at dawn to gather wood for the funeral pyre. Then the Greek leaders sat down to the feast before retiring to bed.

Achilles could not sleep. He lay down on the beach by the waves, groaning with misery, and there his exhausted limbs began to relax. Sleep overcame him, and as it did so the ghost of Patroclus appeared to him in a dream. The ghost criticized Achilles for falling asleep and forgetting his friend, who was unable to pass through the gates of Hades until his body had been burned. Then Patroclus' ghost made one special request:

> One last behest I lay upon thy love:
> Place not my bones, Achilles, far from thine;
> But as we two within thy father's house
> Grew up together, from the day when first
> Menoetius brought me thither, then a boy;
> Since for sore guilt of blood from Opoeis
> I had been exiled, having slain (a child
> Unwitting, and in quarrel o'er our dice),
> My playmate, son of king Amphidamas;
> Then Peleus gave me refuge in his halls,
> And loved me well, and named me to thy side—
> So let one urn now hold the bones of both,
> The golden urn, thy heavenly mother's gift.

Achilles promised he would do everything he was asked, and begged Patroclus to come into his arms one last time to comfort him. He held out his arms, but they embraced the empty air. The ghost had vanished.

Achilles sprang to his feet, absolutely astonished, and exclaimed that it was true: some part of us does survive death—and Patroclus had stood over him all night. Those around him awoke as well, and dawn found them still weeping around the body.

True to his word, Agamemnon sent out the men with mules from all over the camp to fetch wood. When the gathering parties reached Mount Ida they set to with their axes, felling whole trees and splitting them up into logs for the journey back. They laid them on the shore where Achilles had planned his joint grave mound with Patroclus. Achilles ordered his Myrmidons to put on their armor and the charioteers to harness their horses. The chariots then led the procession, followed by the infantry, with the body of Patroclus in the middle, clothed with locks of hair from each of his comrades that they had cut off in his honor. Bringing up the rear, Achilles supported Patroclus' head.

Achilles planned an elaborate
funeral for Patroclus. There was
an enormous funeral pyre,
fueled by the fat of many
sacrificed animals. Patroclus'
favorite dogs and horses went
to death with their master, and
twelve Trojan prisoners were
killed and burned as a tribute.

When they reached the designated spot, Achilles cut an auburn lock from his own hair—the one that his father had promised to cut off as a sacrifice to the gods on his return—and placed it in Patroclus' dead hands. Achilles knew that he would never go home again, and since the gods were not going to grant his father's prayers, he would give the lock of hair to Patroclus. Then Agamemnon sent the troops back to their ships, leaving only the closest friends of Patroclus to prepare for the funeral.

The mourners helped Achilles to pile up the wood and then they laid the body on top. They slaughtered and skinned many sheep and cattle at the foot of the pyre, and Achilles collected their fat and anointed Patroclus' body all over with it. He added two large jars of honey and oil, propping them up on top of the pyre. Then he flung four horses onto it as well, groaning as he did so. Next he slit the throats of two of Patroclus' pet dogs and threw them on. Then Achilles fulfilled his brutal vow to do the same to the twelve Trojan captives that he had brought from the river. Finally, he set light to the pyre, calling out to Patroclus as he did so:

> *All hail, Patroclus! Even in death's abode*
> *I bid thee hail: behold my vows fulfill'd:*
> *Twelve sons of noble Trojans at thy side:*
> *Whom with thee fire devours; but Priam's son,*
> *Hector, to fire I give not, but to dogs.*

Hector's body had been left to the mercy of the dogs, but Aphrodite kept them away, and anointed the body so that its skin should not be torn when Achilles dragged it behind his chariot. Apollo covered the corpse with a dark cloud so that the sun would not cause it to decay.

The funeral pyre would not kindle. On an impulse Achilles prayed to the North Wind and the West Wind, and promised them magnificent sacrifices. When she heard his prayer, the divine messenger Iris dashed off to the winds, Boreas and Zephyr, who were dining together in Zephyr's windy home. She told them that Achilles was praying to them, promising them extraordinary sacrifices. When Iris left, the two winds rose together with a mighty roar, storming over the sea—raising the waves and tossing the ships—until they came to the land of Troy.

There they launched themselves at the funeral pyre making the flames blaze higher. All night long, Achilles poured out libations to them using an enormous two-handled cup, struggling around the pyre and groaning as he went. Finally, as light seeped into the sky, the winds rushed home again, the fire died down, and Achilles sank onto the ground asleep.

FUNERAL PYRES

FOR THE ANCIENT GREEKS, THE FUNERAL PYRE WAS THE CULMINATION OF THEIR RITUALS FOR THE DEAD, AT THE END OF THE PROCESSION OF MUSICAL INSTRUMENTS AND TORCHES. THEN THE MOURNERS STOOD AROUND THE PYRE, AND THE SENIOR MOURNER THREW ON A LIGHTED PINE SOAKED IN OIL—THERE WERE LAWS IN ANCIENT ATHENS ABOUT HOW MUCH FAMILIES WERE ALLOWED TO SPEND ON FUNERAL PYRES. WHEN THE FLAMES DIED DOWN AND WERE COMPLETELY EXTINGUISHED WITH WINE, THE BONES WERE GATHERED TOGETHER AND BURIED.

The chariot race

Achilles was woken by the noise of the Greek commanders gathering around him, and soon he was in his feet again telling them what to do. He urged Agamemnon and the others to put out what remained of the flames with wine, and to collect Patroclus' bones and put them into an urn. They did as he had told them, and drawing a line around the pyre, they covered it with earth and made a mound.

Achilles then brought out many prizes—cauldrons, horses, cattle, and women— from his ship for the funeral games to be held in honor of Patroclus. The first event was to be a chariot race. Achilles addressed the assembled Greeks and announced that he would not be entering his immortal horses in the chariot competition. Patroclus had been kind to the horses, and they were still grieving for him, so Achilles would not be competing. Instead, some of the other Greek leaders stepped forward with their fine horses and chariots: Diomedes, Meriones, Menelaus, Eumelus, and Antilochus, who was given a long speech of good advice from his father Nestor.

The charioteers drew lots for their starting positions and got into order, and Phoenix was appointed umpire. All at once, the racers whipped their horses and were off. Once they had passed the turning point, their driving skills began to show. Eumelus surged ahead, with Diomedes hard on his heels. Diomedes was just about to draw level when Apollo spitefully knocked the whip from his hand, and his horses began to slow. With tears of rage streaming down his face, Diomedes watched Eumelus and his chariot pulling away.

Athena saw what had happened, and chased after Diomedes, handing him his whip back and spurring his horses on. Having done this, she caught up with Eumelus and snapped his harness so that his horses dashed ahead and Eumelus himself was thrown clear and badly bruised. Now Diomedes had the lead, with Menelaus pursuing him. Antilochus was lagging behind, but still urging on his father's horses, warning them in no uncertain terms what would happen if they let him down:

> *Why lag ye thus? I warn you what shall hap:*
> *If of your slackness worse the prize we win,*
> *No more shall ye at royal Nestor's hands*
> *Have tendance, but he straight shall slay you both.*
> *On therefore, on together; whilst I plan*
> *How best to pass him in the narrow way,*
> *There where he scarce can shun me, in the strait.*

The charioteers drew lots for their starting positions and got into order.

A little further on the track narrowed dangerously alongside a gully. Antilochus seized his chance, pressing hard behind Menelaus, and ignoring his shouts that he would upset both of them. Finally Menelaus was forced to slow down to avoid a collision, and Antilochus swept past him.

Although the chariot race was run in honor of Patroclus, it did not stop Athena and Apollo intervening on a petty level, fouling their enemies and giving their favorites unfair advantages.

In the assembly of Greeks, Idomeneus was looking out to see who was winning. He shouted out that Diomedes was in the lead, and that Eumelus must have crashed. Little Ajax rebuked him, claiming that Eumelus was still in the lead and offering to wager a fine cauldron that he was right and Idomeneus was wrong. The two might have come to blows had not Achilles intervened and told them to sit down and await the outcome.

At length Diomedes came home in first place, and lost no time in claiming the woman who was his prize. As he did so Antilochus arrived, with the enraged Menelaus just behind him. Meriones was fourth and Eumelus limped in last. But Achilles took pity on Eumelus and acclaimed him as the best of the charioteers, offering him the second prize.

Antilochus was angry that Eumelus was being awarded his prize, and Menelaus was furious with Antilochus for driving so dangerously. But Achilles soothed Antilochus' rage by giving Eumelus a different prize, and Antilochus apologized to Menelaus for his youthful indiscretion and handed over his prize as a peace offering. Meriones received two gold talents, and Achilles gave the unclaimed prize for fifth place to old Nestor as a mark of comradeship.

The closing games

Achilles set out prizes for further challenges, which met with great enthusiasm and joy from the assembly. He offered a mule as the prize for a boxing contest, with a two-handled urn as the loser's prize. The brilliant fighter Epeius stepped forward and boasted that he would pulverize anyone who challenged him:

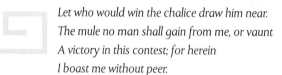

Let who would win the chalice draw him near.
The mule no man shall gain from me, or vaunt
A victory in this contest; for herein
I boast me without peer.

Euryalus stepped up to face Epeius, and the two put up a mighty contest. But Epeius proved the stronger and knocked his opponent down, before sportingly helping him out of the assembly, spitting blood and with his head sagging on one side. Next was the wrestling, and Great Ajax and Odysseus stepped into the middle of the watching troops. This battle between brawn and brain was evenly matched, and neither was able to gain the advantage, until at length Achilles declared a draw and the prizes were shared.

The fourth event was the sprint, with a prize of a silver bowl for mixing wine. Odysseus, Little Ajax and Antilochus lined up to race. The swift Ajax led, until Athena took a hand to help her favorite Odysseus; she caused Ajax to slip in the dung from the cows that had been slaughtered for the funeral, and Odysseus was the winner. Antilochus came last, joking that he had been beaten by a very much older man:

Achilles ordered splendid ceremonial games for Patroclus' funeral; he gave rich prizes (from the treasure given to him from Agamemnon) but he did not take part in the games himself.

I speak but what ye all, my friends, know well.
The Gods delight to honour ancient men.
Ajax is elder scarce than mine own self;
But he, divine Odysseus, who hath won,
Is of the generations now gone by;
A green old age is his; with him to race
Were task to any, save to Peleus' Son.

Next there was a dueling contest, with the prize of the armor that Patroclus had stripped from the body of Sarpedon. Great Ajax and Diomedes fought for this prize, but after a fierce battle a draw was declared as none of the onlookers wished to see their heroes injured. There followed a shot-putting contest, won by Polypoetes, and an archery contest, won by Meriones. Finally the time came for the javelin competition, and Achilles brought out a spear and a valuable brand-new cauldron embossed with flowers as prizes. Agamemnon stepped forward to compete for the coveted honor, along with Idomeneus' attendant Meriones.

But at the last moment, Achilles intervened to stop the contest from going ahead. He acknowledged that his former enemy Agamemnon was the finest wielder of the javelin in the army, and that nobody could compete with him. He gave him the cauldron and asked Meriones if he would accept the spear.

Agamemnon accepted the beautiful cauldron with a bow, and handed it over to his herald. The argument between the two heroes on the Greek side, which had done so much damage and caused the deaths of so many, was at an end.

GAMES

THE GREEKS WERE PARTICULARLY ATTACHED TO COMPETITIVE GAMES, OFTEN ATHLETIC CONTESTS IN RUNNING, JUMPING, THROWING A JAVELIN, AND THROWING A DISCUS. IN THIS EXCLUSIVELY MALE ACTIVITY, ATHLETES COMPETED NAKED, AND OILED THEIR BODIES TO GIVE THEM A SHEEN. THE ANCIENTS ALSO PLAYED MORE SEDATE GAMES SUCH AS DICE AND MARBLES—AN ANCIENT GREEK VASE SHOWS AJAX AND ACHILLES PLAYING CHECKERS.

Book 24
ACHILLES AND PRIAM

Achilles' obsession

At the close of the day the Greeks returned to their ships to sleep. But Achilles could find no rest, tossing and turning in his grief for Patroclus, and weeping over his memories of his comrade. He walked distractedly down the beach and, hoping to find comfort, he lashed Hector's body once again to his chariot and dragged it around the grave mound:

> ... Anon he yoked
> His horses to his car, and hung again
> Hector to trail behind it; and, when so
> Thrice he had dragged him round Patroclus' cairn,
> Again in mire would leave him, stark and prone,
> And seek once more the slumber in his tent.

Even though Hector was dead, he was still watched over by Apollo, who protected his flesh from being torn or damaged by Achilles' mistreatment. Some of the gods urged Hermes to steal Hector's body, but Hera, Poseidon, and Athena forbade it, because they still hated the Trojans. Eleven days went by in the same way, with Achilles brutalizing the body of Hector night after night. On the twelfth day, Apollo begged the gods to have some pity for Hector; he said that—however much they might support Achilles—his obsessive behavior had become a disgrace.

Hera replied with fury: Hector was a mere mortal, but Achilles was the son of a goddess. But Zeus intervened to stop the argument: he said that Hector had always been a favorite of his, and though the plan to steal his body away was impractical—Achilles' mother Thetis was there day and night—he had a solution. He called Thetis to his side from her cavern under the sea, and told her to inform Achilles how angry the gods had grown at his behavior:

Quick hie thee to his camp, and give thy hest;
Tell him, the Gods now murmur, and myself
Beyond all others wrathful, that he still
Holds Hector, in this madness of his soul,
Amongst the long-beak'd barks, nor yields him back.
So may he reverence me, and loose the dead.

Thetis was sent by Zeus to persuade her son to give up the body of Hector so that Priam could bury him properly. Achilles had been keeping it lashed to his chariot, dragging it around Patroclus' grave whenever he was overcome with grief for his dead friend. Even the gods found this too much to bear.

Thetis obediently traveled straight to her son's tent, where she found him groaning and lamenting. She urged him to put aside his misery, since death would soon come to him. Then Thetis told him of Zeus' wrath, and his command that Achilles should accept a ransom for Hector's body. Achilles answered briefly, agreeing that, if it was Zeus' will, the Trojans could have Hector's body back.

HERMES

HERMES WAS THE MESSENGER OF THE GODS, BUT ALSO PRESIDED OVER LUCK AND MUSIC—DICE GAMES AND LYRE-PLAYING IN PARTICULAR. HE WAS PORTRAYED WITH WINGED SANDALS TO SPEED HIM ON HIS JOURNEY, WHICH ALSO MADE HIM THE GOD OF ATHLETICS. HE WAS KNOWN FOR HIS CUNNING, AND HIS ABILITY TO LULL PEOPLE INTO BELIEVING ANYTHING WITH HIS BRILLIANT TALK, WHICH ALSO MADE HIM THE GOD OF MERCHANTS AND SALESPEOPLE.

Priam's embassy

At the same time, Zeus sent his messenger Iris down to Troy to tell Priam to go into the Greek camp, with gifts for Achilles and a wagon to fetch back his son's body. As Iris approached Priam's palace, she could hear the sound of mourning and lamentations, and found the king surrounded by his remaining sons in the courtyard, wrapped in a cloak, his head covered in dung from the ground. Iris told him what Zeus had said, adding Zeus' other instructions: that Priam should go alone and without fear, and that the god Hermes would go with him to protect him. Achilles was not stupid or evil, Iris told Priam, and once he was inside Achilles' tent, he would be perfectly safe.

As soon as Iris had left, Priam ordered his sons to find a mule-wagon and to prepare it for the trip. But when he told his wife Hecabe, she screamed at him that he was absolutely mad. Weren't things bad enough, without him risking his life as well? All they could do, she said, was stay and weep for their son. Priam replied that he was determined to go because he had heard the message from the gods himself:

> *Think not to stay my going; croak not thus*
> *A bird of evil boding in my house.*
> *Thou wilt not move me. Had he been of men,*
> *A seer, an augur-prophet, or a priest,*
> *Then haply we might deem his bidding false,*
> *And put the matter from us. But myself*
> *Beheld the Goddess, heard with mine own ears,*
> *And know her words not vain. Therefore I go ...*

As Priam spoke, he lifted the decorated lids of their storage chests and pulled out twelve beautiful robes and twelve cloaks, as well as sheets, mantles, and tunics to go with them. Then he weighed out gold, and brought out tripods and cauldrons and a beautiful cup that the Thracians had given him—one of his most precious posses-sions. As Priam made these preparations, his mood darkened, and he raged at his sons in the courtyard, calling them cowards and swindlers. If only they had been killed instead of Hector, he wailed.

Terrified of their father, his sons dashed to fetch the wagon, tied a basket to it, and packed in the ransom that Priam had chosen. When it was ready, Hecabe came with a golden cup of wine to ask her husband to offer a libation to Zeus and to pray that he would come home safely. This Priam did, and Zeus heard his prayer and sent an eagle flying right over the city as a good omen to comfort them. Then they were off on their dangerous errand, the wagon in front with a herald driving it and Priam behind, in his own chariot, whipping it through the streets of Troy as fast as he could go. His family followed behind until the old man rumbled out of the gates onto the plain of Troy, and then they turned back to the city, weeping for a man who seemed to be going to his death.

When Zeus saw Priam emerge from the gates, he summoned Hermes and told him to go down and make sure that Priam was not recognized until he reached Achilles' tent. Night was falling as Hermes was carried by his golden sandals all the way to the Hellespont, and he came to earth in the guise of a young man. Priam and his attendant saw him walking toward them and were paralyzed with fright. But Hermes came straight up to them and shook Priam's hand, pretending to be a follower of Achilles' father. Priam begged him for news of Hector's body—whether he was too late and whether it had already been cut into pieces and fed to the dogs. Hermes reassured him: the body was intact and was still lying next to Achilles' tent:

> Nor hound nor bird has yet devour'd thy son.
> Still there beside Achilles' ship he lies
> Whole in mid camp. Though this day's dawn the twelfth
> That riseth o'er him lying stark outstretch'd
> Yet incorrupt he lies, by worms untouch'd
> (Whereto men slain in battle yield a meal).

Priam breathed a sigh of relief and offered Hermes a beautiful cup if he would protect him. Hermes, still pretending to be part of Achilles' entourage, refused the cup but promised his protection nonetheless. And with that he leaped into the chariot, took the reins from Priam and set off toward the Greek defensive wall.

When they reached it, the sentries were preparing their meal, but Hermes put them to sleep, and unlocked the gates so that Priam could go right into the enemy camp.

Priam begged him for news of Hector's body—whether he was too late and whether it had already been cut into pieces and fed to the dogs.

They came to the fence that the Myrmidons had built around Achilles' tent, and Hermes lifted the bar that closed the gate, which was so heavy that it took three men to heave it into place. With Priam safely inside the compound, Hermes leaped down from the chariot, and revealed his real identity. He told Priam to go right inside the tent, to embrace Achilles' knees and speak to him in the name of his own parents and son.

Strange meeting

Priam did as he was advised. He walked in unseen by the other Myrmidons, grasped Achilles' knees in supplication, and kissed the hands that had slaughtered his sons. Achilles was astonished, and now that they could see who their visitor was, the other onlookers were staggered as well. Priam spoke out, and asked Achilles to recall his own father:

> Thy father—O thou image of the Gods,
> Achilles, think of him—then look on me,
> Like him, upon the threshold-step of death.
> Haply the neighbours harry his estate,
> Nor hath he who may drive the ill away.
> Nathless, whilst hearing thou art yet alive,
> He still hath joy at heart, and day by day
> Hath hope to see his son, from Troy return'd.

Sure enough, Priam's words softened Achilles and made him want to weep. He took the old man by the hand, and both of them for a moment were consumed by grief. Then Achilles leaped from his chair and raised Priam to his feet, praising him for his courage for coming alone to the Greek ships. He invited the old man to sit down and talk with him.

Priam refused to sit, but instead demanded back the body of his son in return for the enormous ransom he had brought. Achilles was not pleased and warned Priam not to provoke him:

> *Fret me no more, old man; and know, myself*
> *Am minded to loose Hector. Here to me*
> *A messenger from Zeus my mother came,*
> *The daughter of the elder Ocean-God.*
> *Yea, and full well of mine own wit I know,*
> *O Priam, that a God hath led thy feet*
> *Here 'mid Achaia's barks.*

KING PRIAM

PRIAM WAS KING OF TROY AND HUSBAND OF HECABE. HE WAS THE ELDERLY AND PROUD FATHER OF 50 SONS, 19 OF WHOM WERE THE CHILDREN OF HECABE, INCLUDING HECTOR, PARIS, AND HELENUS. HE BECAME KING AFTER THE SACK OF TROY BY HERACLES, DURING WHICH ALL HIS BROTHERS WERE KILLED, AND NOW HE WAS A TRAGIC FIGURE, ABOUT TO PRESIDE OVER THE SECOND DESTRUCTION OF THE CITY.

Priam did as he was told, and Achilles' attendants went outside and unpacked the wagon, leaving aside a couple of the mantles in which to wrap Hector's body. Achilles called some of his waiting women to wash and anoint the body where Priam could not see it, afraid that the old king might lose control of his anger if he saw the state it was in. When this had been done, Achilles lifted Hector into the wagon, calling out to Patroclus as he did so to forgive his tenderness toward his killer.

Back inside, Achilles told Priam he had done as he demanded, and that at dawn the next day he could take the body away. Then he invited Priam to eat with them, and a sheep was slaughtered for the two of them and their attendants. After they had eaten everything they wanted, Achilles and Priam stared at each other across the remains of the feast. Priam was impressed with how tall Achilles was, and how good-looking, while Achilles found himself admiring Priam's nobility and bearing.

Achilles organized beds on the portico for both Priam and his driver, asking the king to sleep outside in case some colleague should arrive and discover his presence. He also offered to call a truce for as many days as Priam wanted to celebrate Hector's funeral. Priam replied gratefully, and asked for nine days to mourn, one day for the funeral and another to build the grave mound:

> *Thou know'st how we are leaguer'd in our walls,*
> *And how the hill is far from whence to fetch*
> *The fagots, and the people fear to fetch.*
> *Suffer then that for nine days in our homes*
> *We make our wail, but on the tenth we give*
> *His burial, on the eleventh rear his cairn;*
> *So on the twelfth to war, since war we must.*

All the while,

his wife

Andromache

held his head

in her hands,

singing a song

of misery

about the fate

of Troy.

Achilles agreed, and shook Priam's hand to reassure him. Then both sides settled down for the night after their extraordinary meeting, Priam on the porch and Achilles inside, with his hard-won Briseis beside him.

Priam's return

Hermes woke the king, and warned him that the Trojans would need three times as much ransom if Agamemnon were to find him. Alarmed, Priam roused his attendant, and Hermes harnessed the mules and drove them quickly back unseen through the camp. When they reached the Xanthus River, Hermes returned to Olympus. As dawn rose, the two headed toward the city, alone with their burden.

Cassandra was the first to see the sad procession, and she urged the citizens of Troy to welcome Hector home as they had never welcomed him before. Soon the whole town was on the move, rushing out through the gates to greet Priam and the body. They took Hector's body into his palace, and laid it on a bed; poets and women came to chant dirges. All the while, Andromache held his head in her hands, singing a song of misery about the fate of Troy and of her son—one doomed to fall to the Greeks, the other doomed to be taken in the Greek ships home in slavery:

> *Accursed, accursed the anguish thou hast left,*
> *O Hector, to thy parents, but beyond*
> *Ev'n theirs, the wretchedness thou leav'st to me!*

Priam came in supplication to
Achilles to beg him for the body
of his dead son Hector. The
corpse was hidden behind a
drape, so that Priam could not see
how Achilles had dishonored it.

Who dying couldst not stretch thy hand to mine,
Nor speak me one kind word, to be for aye
Remember'd mid my weepings, nights and days!

Then Hecabe, Hector's mother, spoke proudly of her son, the dearest of all her
children, surely beloved of the gods. At last she had him back again:

And now I have thee, to thy home given back
As dewy-fresh and taintless, as a babe
Oe'r whom the Godhead of the silver bow
Hath pass'd with gentle darts, and, painless, slain.

Then she could speak no more. In her turn, Helen praised Hector for his kindness,
for defending her against resentful Trojans, and never speaking a harsh word to her.

Priam urged his people to collect wood for the funeral pyre, assuring them of
Achilles' promise for a truce, and for the next nine days, they gathered fuel. Early on
the tenth day, they laid Hector's body on the enormous pyre and set it alight.

When the pyre had burned itself out, the Trojans collected Hector's bones,
wrapped them in purple shrouds, and put them in a coffin made of gold. They buried
him quickly and piled the earth on top into a mound, with sentries posted around to
warn of a surprise attack by the Greeks. Then they returned into the city and gathered
together at an enormous funeral feast held in the palace of King Priam.

And so they buried Hector, the hero of Troy.

WHAT HAPPENED NEXT?

The death of Achilles

After Hector's death, the Trojan forces were boosted by the arrival of the Amazons, led by their queen, Penthesilea, and the Ethiopians, led by King Memnon. Achilles killed both leaders, but regretted the death of Penthesilea, with whom he had fallen in love in the heat of battle. Not long after, Achilles himself was killed, shot through the heel, his only vulnerable spot. Paris fired the arrow, but it was guided by Apollo. Great Ajax heroically defended Achilles' corpse from the Trojans; he believed he was the true heir to Achilles' god-given armor, but Odysseus challenged him. The Greeks staged a contest, and Ajax lost. He went mad and killed himself—although some sources say that he was mysteriously murdered.

FURTHER ADVENTURES OF ODYSSEUS

The wily Odysseus continued his stealth campaign against Troy. Helenus, a son of Priam, was captured by the Greeks; he was a respected seer, and he told them that Troy would never fall until the bow of Heracles was brought to Troy. As it was now in the possession of Philoctetes, Odysseus and Diomedes went to Lemnos to fetch him. Odysseus also brought Neoptolemus, the son of Achilles, to Troy and gave him his father's god-made armor. So the wounded archer came to Troy, was cured by the healer Machaon, and felled Paris with a poisoned arrow loosed from Heracles' bow. Helen was quickly married off to Deiphobus, to keep her in Troy.

Having got rid of Paris, but still not brought Troy to its knees, Odysseus and Diomedes now hatched a plan to infiltrate the city in secret and steal the Palladium, the sacred statue of Athena thought to be the source of the Trojans' endurance. They were successful, but still Troy did not fall; so Odysseus came up with the idea of the wooden horse.

THE TROJAN HORSE

Epeius the architect constructed a horse large enough to hold forty fighting men and dazzling enough to impress the Trojans. It was left out on the plain, in full view, and the Greeks boarded their ships and set sail. However, they only went as far as the island of Tenedos. They left behind a double agent, Sinon, crouching below the horse, looking convincingly beaten up. He told the Trojans that the Greeks had sailed away, leaving the horse to appease Athena; she was angry about the theft of the Palladium, and they wanted her to grant them a safe return. Sinon also told the Trojans that the Greeks had deliberately made the horse too big for the Trojans to steal and take into the city. The Trojans immediately moved heaven and earth to get the horse into the city, tearing down part of their own walls. Only the priest Laocoön and Priam's daughter, Cassandra, advised against this, and they were soon shouted down—Laocoön and his sons were devoured by a sea monster for their presumption. The horse was dragged inside the city and the Trojans celebrated. When they were asleep, Sinon whistled a signal, the warriors in the horse jumped out, and, led by Odysseus, alerted the waiting fleet.

THE END OF TROY

The Greeks were pitiless in their destruction of the city and the people in it. They attacked everybody, men, women, children, asleep or awake, and even defiled the temples, raping and killing in the sacred spaces. The city was burnt to the ground, and all the treasure looted. Priam was slaughtered at the altar by Neoptolemus. Astyanax, Hector's child, was thrown off the battlements. All the women were taken prisoner except Helen, who was returned to Menelaus. Cassandra was given to Agamemnon, and Andromache, Hector's widow, to Neoptolemus, the son of his killer. The only Trojan to get away—because it was destined—was Aeneas, son of Anchises and Aphrodite. He escaped carrying his father on his back, and wandered the Mediterranean, stopping off at Carthage. Eventually he landed in what is now Italy, and established Lavinium, the center of the Latin league, the precursor of Rome.

AFTERMATH

The gods were extremely angry that the Greeks had sacked Troy so thoroughly, especially resenting the sacrilegious treatment of the temples, and they punished the returning heroes heavily. A storm almost destroyed the entire fleet. Menelaus was blown off course, ending up in Egypt; Agamemnon was murdered by his wife Clytemnestra and her lover Aegisthus, in revenge for his sacrifice of Iphigenia; and Odysseus, so central to the Greek victory, famously wandered the seas for another ten years trying to get back home to Ithaca.

Further Reading

TRANSLATIONS OF THE *ILIAD*

Cordery, J. G., *The Iliad of Homer: A Translation* (Rivingtons, 1871) out of print

Fagles, Robert (trans.), *Homer: The Iliad* (Penguin USA, 1998)

Fitzgerald, Robert (trans.), *Homer: The Iliad* (Farrar Straus & Giroux, 2004)

Lattimore, Richmond (trans.), *The Iliad of Homer* (University of Chicago Press, 1961)

FURTHER STUDY OF THE *ILIAD*

Edwards, Mark, *Homer: Poet of the Iliad* (John Hopkins University Press, 1987)

Willcock, Malcolm, M., *A Companion to the Iliad: Based on the translation by Richmond Lattimore* (University of Chicago Press, 1976)

GREEK MYTHOLOGY

Harris, Stephen L. and Platzner, Gloria, *Classical Mythology: Images and Insights* (McGraw-Hill, 2004)

Martin, Richard P., *Myths of the Ancient Greeks* (New American Library, 2003)

Woodford, Susan, *The Trojan War in Ancient Art* (Cornell University Press, 1993)

AUDIO BOOKS

Fagles, Robert (trans.), Derek Jacobi (narrator), *Homer: The Iliad* (Penguin Books Ltd., 1993)

Lattimore, Richmond (trans.), Antony Quayle (reader), *Homer: The Iliad* (HarperAudio, 1996)

Index

Acknowledgments

The authors and Ivy Press would like to thank
Christopher Burns and Dennis Blandford for
all their time, assistance, and expert advice.